CIRIA C602   D0587369   London, 2004

CDM Regulations –
practical guidance for clients and clients' agents

Second edition
Taking account of the ACoP HSG224 (2001)

Prepared by WS Atkins Consultants

Updated by Alan Gilbertson

CIRIA *sharing knowledge ■ building best practice*

Classic House, 174–180 Old Street, London EC1V 9BP, UK
TEL +44 (0)20 7549 3300   FAX +44 (0)20 7253 0523
EMAIL enquiries@ciria.org
WEBSITE www.ciria.org

Summary

The Construction (Design and Management) Regulations 1994 (CDM) apply to nearly all construction work undertaken in the UK. This book helps clients and their advisers understand the role that a client must, by law, play in a construction project which is carried out on his behalf. The legal duties are explained in detail and advice given on how they may be discharged effectively. This new edition takes account of the 2001 approved code of practice (HSE publication HSG224), which has legal status and includes guidance on different procurement methods such as PFI.

CIRIA C602 begins by setting the scene for clients who are not familiar with CDM, referring to later chapters for more detail. It addresses the issues of when the Regulations apply and who is a client and what is a client's agent, before setting out the client's roles and responsibilities under CDM and considering each of them in detail. The book also looks at the documents particular to CDM – the health and safety plan and the health and safety file – and ends with a discussion of contractual issues.

CDM Regulations – practical guidance for clients and clients' agents

1st edition author: WS Atkins Consultants
2nd edition reviser: Gilbertson, A

CIRIA publication C602   1st edn © CIRIA 1998; 2nd edn revisions © CIRIA 2004
First published 1998 as Report 172; updated and revised 2004   ISBN 0-86017-602-9

British Library Cataloguing in Publication Data

A catalogue record for this book is available from the British Library.

Keywords		
Construction management, health and safety		
Construction (Design and Management) Regulations, CDM, client, client's agent, planning supervisor, designer, principal contractor, health and safety file, health and safety plan		

Reader interest	Classification	
Construction industry professionals, health and safety professionals, consultants, contractors, clients, clients' agents, architects, local authorities, government agencies, government	Availability	Unrestricted
	Content	Original research
	Status	Committee-guided
	User	Clients for construction and building work, clients' agents under the CDM Regulations 1994, construction industry professionals

Published by CIRIA, Classic House, 174–180 Old Street, London EC1V 9BP, UK.

About this guide

The CDM Regulations

This book is a practical guide for clients to the Construction (Design and Management) Regulations, known as the "CDM Regulations" or "CDM" for short. The Regulations are a major development in health and safety legislation and affect nearly all construction work of any significance. The role and duties of the client are recognised and clearly stated. Any client of the building/construction industry may be affected, but domestic clients have no responsibilities under the Regulations.

Readership

The guide is written for an intending client of the construction industry, that is, one who will be responsible for commissioning construction work. It can be read both by those approaching the industry for the first time or with only limited knowledge of what is involved and also by more experienced clients. It is also intended for a client's agent under CDM – that is, an agent whom a client appoints to carry out some or all of that client's roles under CDM.

Other construction industry professionals, such as planning supervisors and designers, are likely to find the book useful.

Domestic clients (see Glossary), who will not be letting out accommodation or using their premises for any work-related purpose, are not directly affected by CDM. If they are in any doubt, however, they should seek advice from professional advisers or the Health and Safety Executive (HSE) (see Section 1.2.2).

For simplicity and clarity, a client or client's agent is often addressed in this guide as "you", or referred to as "he"; in practice either or both may be male, female or a corporate entity.

Content

The book provides rapid access to an explanation of how the Regulations affect clients and clients' agents. It examines:

- the scope of the CDM Regulations
- duties under the CDM Regulations
- how clients need to respond to the CDM Regulations.

Terminology

The Regulations have generated some new terms. The most important ones are defined in Chapter 1 and also in the Glossary.

References

It is not the intention to repeat information that is readily available elsewhere, but rather to explain in a practical manner how the Regulations affect clients and to deal with the various points of interpretation.

Where appropriate, references are provided to the Regulations, the associated approved code of practice (ACoP), to other CIRIA publications and to other sections in this guide.

The ACoP

Advice in HSG224 *Managing health and safety in construction: Construction (Design and Management) Regulations 1994* (HSE, 2001), which contains the approved code of practice and related guidance, has particular significance.

1. The code of practice itself is in bold type; it gives practical advice on how to comply with the law with respect to the matters covered, although you may use other methods if they enable you to comply with the law.

2. Other guidance is in normal type; much of it is an interpretation of good practice (using terms such as "should" and "need to"), but some is an interpretation of the law ("must").

In practice, it is safer to apply all of HSG224 as written. As HSG224 is commonly referred to as "the ACoP" and is numbered by paragraph regardless of whether the text is approved code or guidance, reference to the paragraphs in HSG224 is in the style "ACoP para N".

> **Note that the current ACoP (HSG224) replaced the original 1994 ACoP (L54) in 2001; it is substantially different and was the prime driver for the preparation of this publication (CIRIA C602), which itself replaces CIRIA's earlier Report 172.**

How to use this guide

This guide (CIRIA C602) focuses on the issues arising from CDM as they affect clients and (if appointed) clients' agents.

It has been structured so that it can be used both by those who wish to read it from cover to cover and by those who simply need to dip in to look for specific information. It is divided into chapters that focus on key issues. The text is repeated where appropriate, so that each chapter is reasonably self-contained, reducing the need for cross-references.

Chapter 1 – What every client needs to know and do

Chapter 1 is designed to help clients who are not familiar with CDM to gain a rapid understanding of the subject. This chapter explains what the CDM Regulations are and how they affect clients. It provides an overview of the issues arising from CDM and refers to later chapters for further detail. It examines the decisions that clients will have to make and answers typical questions.

Chapter 2 – When and how do the Regulations apply?

Briefly explains the background to CDM and how it applies in different situations.

Chapter 3 – Who is a client and what is a client's agent?

Considers who exactly may be the client for a project and their role in managing hazard and risk. Explains how the role of a client's agent arises. **Note**: the term "client's agent" in this guide should not be confused with the general use of this term.

Chapter 4 – Roles and responsibilities

Examines a client's duties in more depth and the responses to CDM. The duties of the other parties are also briefly explained, for reference.

Chapter 5 – The phases of a construction project

Outlines how CDM affects all phases of the life of a project.

Chapter 6 – Making appointments and judging "competence and resources"

Examines how clients can ensure that they make appointments that meet the requirements of CDM.

Chapter 7 – The health and safety plan

Although clients are not involved in most of the activity leading to the preparation of health and safety plans, they need to understand this process and be able to address certain key issues; this chapter explores these matters from a client's point of view.

Chapter 8 – The health and safety file

As with Chapter 7, clients need both to understand the purpose and scope of health and safety files and be prepared to state their requirements.

Chapter 9 – Legal and contractual issues

Although detailed aspects of legal and contractual issues are beyond the scope of this guide, this chapter outlines some of the issues involved.

Glossary

Explains terms that have a particular meaning in the context of CDM.

Key references

Provided for those clients who wish to study CDM in more detail.

Contents

ABOUT THIS GUIDE 3

1   What every client needs to know and do 13

1.1   THE CDM REGULATIONS.. 13
    1.1.1   Aim of the Regulations... 13
    1.1.2   Who is a client under CDM?... 14
    1.1.3   How the Regulations affect clients..................................... 14

1.2   KEY CLIENT DECISIONS 16
    1.2.1   Strategy and tactics... 16
    1.2.2   Getting help... 16
    1.2.3   Getting involved.. 17
    1.2.4   Keeping control... 17
    1.2.5   Procurement method and forms of contract...................... 18
    1.2.6   Making appointments.. 18
    1.2.7   Assessing competence and resources.................................. 19
    1.2.8   Client's agent... 20
    1.2.9   Designers.. 20
    1.2.10   Planning supervisor 21
    1.2.11   Principal contractor... 22
    1.2.12   Contractors.. 23
    1.2.13   Interfaces... 23
    1.2.14   Providing information.. 24
    1.2.15   Providing adequate time.. 24
    1.2.16   Health and safety plan 24
    1.2.17   Health and safety file 24
    1.2.18   Motivation.. 25
    1.2.19   Avoiding and resolving disputes... 25

2   When and how do the Regulations apply? 27

2.1   WHEN DO THE REGULATIONS APPLY?... 27
    2.1.1   Introduction... 27
    2.1.2   Application.. 27
    2.1.3   What is construction work?... 28
    2.1.4   What is a structure?.. 28
    2.1.5   Exclusions.. 29
    2.1.6   Cleaning work.. 29
    2.1.7   Work for domestic clients... 29
    2.1.8   Local authority as enforcing authority 29
    2.1.9   Work on fixed plant with safe access 30
    2.1.10   Site survey, exploration and investigation......................... 30
    2.1.11   Mineral extraction... 30
    2.1.12   Work off-site.. 30
    2.1.13   Other exclusions.. 30
    2.1.14   Demolition and dismantling 32
    2.1.15   Maintenance.. 32
    2.1.16   Term maintenance... 32
    2.1.17   Archaeology... 32

	2.1.18	Landscaping	32
	2.1.19	Scaffolding	33
	2.1.20	Offshore installations	33
	2.1.21	Mixed projects	33
	2.1.22	Insurance	33
	2.1.23	The "four people on site" rule	33
	2.1.24	Designers' duties	33
2.2	WHEN DOES THE HSE HAVE TO BE NOTIFIED?		33
	2.2.1	What is notification?	33
	2.2.2	Which projects are notifiable?	34
	2.2.3	Who should notify and when?	34
	2.2.4	The 30 days rule	34
	2.2.5	The 500 person-days rule	34
2.3	INTERPRETATION		34
	2.3.1	Start of a project	34
	2.3.2	Changing circumstances	35
	2.3.3	Making decisions	35

3 Who is a client and what is a client's agent? **37**

3.1	THE REGULATIONS		37
	3.1.1	Definitions	37
	3.1.2	Developers	38
	3.1.3	Competence of a client's agent	38
	3.1.4	Role of a client's agent	38
3.2	THE ROLE OF A CLIENT IN MANAGING HAZARD AND RISK		39
	3.2.1	The client's role	39
	3.2.2	Benefits to the client	39
3.3	EXAMPLES		39
	3.3.1	Joint venture	39
	3.3.2	The new client	40
	3.3.3	Client's representative	40
	3.3.4	Tenants	40
	3.3.5	Utilities	40
	3.3.6	PFI project	41

4 Roles and responsibilities **43**

4.1	THE PARTIES TO CDM		43
	4.1.1	Who are the parties to CDM?	43
	4.1.2	How do the parties relate to each other?	43
4.2	CLIENT'S DUTIES		45
	4.2.1	Introduction	45
	4.2.2	Making appointments	45
	4.2.3	Providing information	45
	4.2.4	Allowing work to start on site	45
	4.2.5	Holding the health and safety file and making it available	45
	4.2.6	Other roles	46
4.3	A CLIENT'S RESPONSE		46
	4.3.1	Organisation	46
	4.3.2	Procedures	46

4.4   OTHER PARTIES' DUTIES (IN BRIEF) 47
        4.4.1   Designers 47
        4.4.2   Planning supervisor 47
        4.4.3   Principal contractor 47
        4.4.4   Contractors 48
        4.4.5   Health and Safety Executive 48

5   The phases of a construction project 49
    5.1   PLANNING 49
            5.1.1   Inception activities 49
            5.1.2   Strategy for compliance 49
            5.1.3   Start of a project 49
            5.1.4   Project programme 49
            5.1.5   Project budget 50

    5.2   DESIGN 50
            5.2.1   Appointments 50
            5.2.2   Provision of information 50
            5.2.3   Scheme design 51
            5.2.4   Detailed design 51
            5.2.5   Planning applications, building regulations etc 51
            5.2.6   Other health and safety legislation 51
            5.2.7   Pre-tender health and safety plan 51

    5.3   CONSTRUCTION 51
            5.3.1   Selection of contractors 51
            5.3.2   Appointments 51
            5.3.3   Construction plan 52
            5.3.4   Ongoing design 52
            5.3.5   Construction 52
            5.3.6   Commissioning 52
            5.3.7   Health and safety file 52
            5.3.8   End of the project 52

    5.4   POST-CONSTRUCTION ACTIVITIES 53
            5.4.1   Rectification of defects 53
            5.4.2   Post-construction works 53
            5.4.3   Cleaning 53
            5.4.4   Health and safety file 53

6   Making appointments and judging "competence and resources" 55
    6.1   MAKING APPOINTMENTS 55
            6.1.1   The Regulations 55
            6.1.2   Timing 56
            6.1.3   Form of appointment 56
            6.1.4   Changing appointments 57
            6.1.5   Nomination 57
            6.1.6   Subcontracts 57
            6.1.7   Overseas companies 57

    6.2   JUDGING COMPETENCE AND RESOURCES 58
            6.2.1   Sources of information 58
            6.2.2   How to judge 58
            6.2.3   Time as a resource 59
            6.2.4   Money as a resource 60

6.3 EXAMPLES OF GOOD PRACTICE...60
    6.3.1   Demolition...60
    6.3.2   Shop fit-out..61
    6.3.3   New-build office...61
    6.3.4   Refurbishment..62
    6.3.5   Emergency repairs 62

7 The health and safety plan 63

7.1 LIFE CYCLE OF THE HEALTH AND SAFETY PLAN 63
    7.1.1   Introduction 63
    7.1.2   The pre-tender health and safety plan....................................63
    7.1.3   The construction health and safety plan 63
    7.1.4   Acceptance for work to start on site.......................................63
    7.1.5   Completion...63

7.2 FEATURES OF THE HEALTH AND SAFETY PLAN..............................64
    7.2.1   An appropriate health and safety plan 64
    7.2.2   Pre-tender health and safety plan 64
    7.2.3   Construction health and safety plan.......................................65
    7.2.4   Non-standard situations..65

8 The health and safety file 67

8.1 WHAT IS THE HEALTH AND SAFETY FILE?.......................................67
    8.1.1   Introduction 67

8.2 PREPARATION OF THE FILE 67
    8.2.1   The client's role..67
    8.2.2   What does it contain?..67
    8.2.3   What format and medium should be adopted? 68
    8.2.4   How it is organised?...68
    8.2.5   Who prepares it?...69
    8.2.6   How and when is it assembled? 69
    8.2.7   How is it made available?...69

8.3 CLIENT'S REQUIREMENTS...70
    8.3.1   Introduction 70
    8.3.2   Holding the file and retrieving information 70
    8.3.3   Leaseholders...70
    8.3.4   Disposal of property...70
    8.3.5   Updating the file 71
    8.3.6   Further guidance 71

9 Legal and contractual issues 73

9.1 LEGAL AND CONTRACTUAL ISSUES..73
    9.1.1   Client responsibilities 73
    9.1.2   Sanctions..73
    9.1.3   What does the client have to do?..73
    9.1.4   Resources...74
    9.1.5   Contracts..74
    9.1.6   Statutory contractual relationships...74
    9.1.7   Client's "named person" 74

9.2		TERMS OF APPOINTMENT	74
	9.2.1	General	74
	9.2.2	Commercial	75
	9.2.3	Client's agent	75
	9.2.4	Designers	75
	9.2.5	Planning supervisor	75
	9.2.6	Principal contractor	75
	9.2.7	Contractors	76
9.3		THE ACoP	76
	9.3.1	Status	76
9.4		PROCUREMENT ROUTES	76
	9.4.1	Traditional	76
	9.4.2	Turnkey and design-and-build	76
	9.4.3	Construction management and management contracting	77
	9.4.4	DBFO and PFI	77
	9.4.5	PPP	77
	9.4.6	Partnering, term and call-off	77
	9.4.7	Maintenance contracts	78
	9.4.8	Small jobs	78

Glossary	**79**
References	**83**
ACKNOWLEDGEMENTS	85

List of figures

Figure 1	The application of CDM	31
Figure 2	How CDM duty-holders relate to a client	44

1   What every client needs to know and do

1.1   THE CDM REGULATIONS

1.1.1   Aim of the Regulations

The Construction (Design and Management) Regulations 1994, known as the CDM Regulations, aim to reduce the incidence of accidents and occupational ill-health arising from construction work. Introduction of the Regulations caused procedures to be put in place, improving the planning and management of health and safety on construction projects of all types, throughout every phase and involving all parties (client, designer, contractor and subcontractor) in the management of hazard and risk.

The Regulations place specific duties on each party as well as a general duty to co-operate and communicate. Moreover, only those who are competent and adequately resourced to discharge their CDM duties are to be appointed.

To facilitate this, new roles and management tools have been created, as in the box below.

THE ROLE OF PLANNING SUPERVISOR whose duties relate principally to the co-ordination of health and safety issues during project design and planning.

THE ROLE OF PRINCIPAL CONTRACTOR whose duties relate mainly to the co-ordination of health and safety issues during construction.

THE HEALTH AND SAFETY PLAN, which communicates health and safety information both pre-tender (from designers and the client, for contractors) and during construction (planning and management of the work on site).

THE HEALTH AND SAFETY FILE, which records essential health and safety information from the design and construction process. This is passed to the client to be kept available for use by others involved in future work on the structure.

A diagram showing how the various parties to CDM relate to each other may be found in Figure 2 (Chapter 4, p 44).

For those new to CDM, the requirements and new terminology can appear daunting and – particularly on smaller projects – out of proportion. However, the construction industry is now learning how to undertake CDM duties in a manner that is proportionate to project size and level of risk. The Regulations contain frequent reference to duties being performed "so far as is reasonably practicable", which means that a sense of proportion and professional judgement are required.

> The key object of the Regulations is to ensure construction health and safety risks are avoided, mitigated or managed. This does not necessarily entail bureaucratic form-filling or lengthy documents, which often conceal health and safety issues.

Clients should benefit in several ways. Planning and control should be tighter, very hazardous tasks largely removed, communication should be improved, and more attention given to safe access and maintenance. Moreover, where appropriate, the duties of the planning supervisor can be undertaken by a project manager or lead designer and the duties of the principal contractor can be undertaken by the main/managing contractor.

1.1.2 Who is a client under CDM?

A client is an organisation or individual for whom a construction project is carried out, whether by others or in-house. Domestic clients have no CDM duty.

The ACoP (paras 56–57) notes that a wide range of bodies may be clients under CDM, including local authorities, school governors, insurance companies, developers and PFI project originators. The key questions to consider when identifying who is the client for CDM purposes are:

- who is at the head of the procurement chain?
- who arranges for the design work?
- who engages contractors?

The rules governing whether CDM places duties upon clients and their appointees relate mainly to the scale of the work; details are given in Chapter 2.

Designers have duties under the Regulations that apply to all their work – and one of the duties of designers is to advise clients of their duties under the Regulations. (Clients who intend to carry out their own design must ensure that the people responsible are competent and adequately resourced and are instructed to comply with the Regulations.)

Clients who have a series of small projects, often undertaken under term contracts or similar arrangements, have to decide whether to apply CDM to all the projects or only those that would individually trigger CDM. This is discussed in Chapter 9.

Clients should be aware that where the Regulations apply, the HSE may need to be notified (see Section 2.2).

1.1.3 How the Regulations affect clients

A client has specific duties under CDM, which are as follows:

- appointing a planning supervisor and a principal contractor
- making reasonable enquiries before appointment to check that potential service providers are competent and adequately resourced as regards health and safety
- providing health and safety information about the project and site
- not permitting construction work to start on site until an adequate construction health and safety plan is available
- holding the health and safety file and making it available to others once the project is handed over.

See Chapter 4 for further details of client's duties and note that clients can (if they wish) appoint a "client's agent" to undertake their duties. This is explained in Chapter 3.

The benefits of CDM to clients are:

- a reduction in accidents and ill-health among construction workers and others affected by construction, due to the better management of risk

- improved planning and co-ordination between designers and improved exchange of information

- safe future work assured by the need to consider safe access and avoidance of health hazards for future maintenance and cleaning as an integral aspect of design

- as a result of all the above, a reduction in the overall cost of construction.

Clients may incur some additional costs as a result of CDM because:

- there are specific functions that have to be fulfilled by specific new duty-holders

- some construction may cost more to ensure that it is carried out to higher safety standards and to avoid health hazards.

Clients should seek to control costs and gain benefit by adopting a strategy to suit each project by:

- responding in a manner proportional to the risks on the project and the difficulty of managing those risks

- seeking to comply with Regulations in a manner consistent with the other goals of the project, reinforcing co-ordination and co-operation for the benefit of the project as a whole

- putting in place arrangements for CDM that relate to the overall project organisation, so that powers and responsibilities are aligned and disputes can be resolved.

If the management processes involved in CDM (planning, co-operating, communicating) are undertaken in appropriately, as part of the overall management of the project, the balance of costs and benefits should be favourable, due to:

- closer co-operation between designers

- improved buildability on site

- less time and money lost through accidents and ill-health

- more predictable out-turn cost and programme

- better records (information) for use in the future

- lower maintenance and cleaning costs.

In recent years there has been a series of initiatives intended to improve working relationships within the construction industry, including a move towards greater co-operation and the integration of teams. In the same way, CDM aimed to bring a new approach to the management of risk in health and safety in the industry. These aims are complementary.

If the intentions behind CDM are to be achieved, clients will need to make sensible decisions and ensure that their advisers are committed to the same goals. The rest of this chapter examines the decisions each client will have to make in response to CDM.

1.2   KEY CLIENT DECISIONS

1.2.1   Strategy and tactics

The Regulations made in 1994 and amended in 2000 are reproduced in the Health and Safety Commission's publication *Managing health and safety in construction* (HSC, 2001). This includes the approved code of practice (ACoP) and contains authoritative advice. In addition, other CIRIA publications in this series may be consulted (see References).

In deciding how best to respond to the statutory requirements of CDM, clients will have many other aspects of their projects in mind; their response to CDM should not be made in isolation and should be in proportion to the risks.

> The client's response to CDM does not need to dominate the procurement strategy but should be integral within it. Providing their advisers are appropriately competent and resourced, the requirements of CDM should be easily achieved.

1.2.2   Getting help

In most cases competent construction professionals will be able to advise their clients about CDM. The HSE has several local area offices, which may be found under "Health and Safety Executive" in the telephone directory. The HSE also runs a helpline, tel: 08701 545 500; fax: 02920 559 260; email: hseinfomationservice@natbrit.com. HSE's website address is: <www.hse.gov.uk>.

Some clients will wish to develop their in-house expertise. Others will wish to appoint a client's agent (see Chapter 3) for one or more of the following reasons:

- the client does not have or wish to develop the expertise

- the client does not wish to rely only on the advice of his designer(s) and planning supervisor

- the client does not wish to take responsibility for meeting his duties

- there is no single identifiable client and the use of a client's agent is a practical way of ensuring that the CDM duties are carried out.

> **Note**: The term "client's agent" in this guide should not be confused with the general use of this term.

If a client's agent is appointed (see Chapter 3 for how to go about this), a client will still be expected to meet any obligations not delegated to the agent. These might include:

- providing information about the site

- discharging non-CDM health and safety responsibilities

- making available the health and safety file (see Chapter 8) to those who need it in the future.

Experience has shown that most clients are in fact able to carry out a client's CDM duties without appointing an agent. Even though duties may be delegated, clients should be aware that the court may decide that a client still has some responsibilities (see Chapter 9).

1.2.3   Getting involved

If a client decides not to appoint an agent, or if he is considering undertaking other roles (designer, planning supervisor, principal contractor, contractor), then he must have or be able to call on adequate competence and resource for the duties to be undertaken (see Chapter 6).

The decision on whether to undertake a role will be affected by:

- a client's wish to be in control
- the experience and skills of his staff
- the nature and scale of the construction work to be undertaken.

> In general, most clients should be able to undertake the duties of client with the advice and assistance of their designer(s) and planning supervisor. The other roles will require a greater knowledge and skill, depending on the complexity of the project and the risks involved.

1.2.4   Keeping control

Experienced clients with staff skilled in health and safety matters may wish to undertake not only a client's duties but also one or more of the roles of designer, planning supervisor and (possibly) principal contractor. For example, a large manufacturer with an in-house technical and facilities management team (which manages all projects undertaken on the site) may decide to be client and designer, and also to undertake the duties of planning supervisor and (if he has staff experienced in managing construction) principal contractor, for most or all projects on his site.

For clients who do not have a strong in-house team, and who appoint an external project manager for major construction work, it may make sense to appoint the project manager as client's agent (if one is needed) as he will, in any case, be acting for them on a day-to-day basis. If so, the project manager must have the necessary authority.

On the other hand, where smaller works (maintenance or refurbishment etc) will be project-managed in-house, some clients will wish their in-house managers to develop the skills rather than appoint others to carry out their CDM duties.

Any project manager's duties should include the melding of all the parties' CDM roles together, including careful attention to how the boundaries of their duties will be dealt with in their contracts. (See also Section 1.2.13 and Chapter 9.)

Some clients with in-house teams may decide to put in place mechanisms for improving the management of design and construction (including asking for monitoring, reviews, audits etc) to ensure CDM compliance on their projects. This is not a requirement of the Regulations. The planning supervisor and the principal contractor are already charged with co-ordinating health and safety, during the design and construction phases, of designers and contractors.

Another aspect of keeping control is the need to focus the duty-holders (whoever they may be) on the essentials of CDM and to insist upon concise, relevant documentation that will meet the requirements of the Regulations without burying the project in paper.

Procurement method and forms of contract

There is no reason why CDM should affect the choice of procurement method. Once the choice has been made, the Regulations are sufficiently adaptable to be applied in a sensible manner. With each form of procurement, parties' actions under CDM could cut across contractual relationships (such as when a planning supervisor's interventions affect performance to programme). There is little experience of this being problematic.

If a client has a term contractor or other partnership arrangements, the manner in which CDM is handled will need to be agreed and arrangements put in place. The fact that all the general issues can be dealt with in advance with only project-specific matters needing to be revisited, will speed and smooth the execution of projects.

Although CDM arrangements need to apply only to those projects that trigger CDM, there may be advantages in applying CDM procedures to *all* projects, so that:

* common procedures are used

* the CDM framework ensures that hazards and risks are properly addressed (as required by other health and safety legislation)

* information and site rules are made available in a formal manner

* management of health and safety on site is to a common standard

* health and safety files are kept up-to-date for each structure.

The authorities producing standard forms of contract have produced addenda or revised forms to deal with CDM. However, the approaches taken vary and expert advice should be sought (see also Chapter 9).

Making appointments

There is no reason why CDM should significantly affect the way that designers and contractors are appointed. The only requirements are that:

* the specific CDM appointments of planning supervisor and principal contractor (and client's agent if required) must be made. Often appointees will be members of the client's normal team of advisers or the main or managing contractor

* the client or his agent must be satisfied that his appointees are competent at, and adequately resourced for, handling health and safety issues; he may do this (see Chapter 6) but may look to the planning supervisor for advice.

Neither the Regulations nor the ACoP mention the order in which appointments are to be made under CDM. Normally, designers will be appointed first. It may not be feasible to specify the competence required of designers or planning supervisors until some design has been done to indicate the technical character of the project. A client wishing to rely upon advisers for the assessment of competence and resources may wish to appoint a planning supervisor first, with the duty under the Regulations to advise upon designers' competence and resources – but how can the client assess the planning supervisor? Similarly, if the client decides to appoint a client's agent, how can he assess his competence and resources?

This difficulty could be overcome by first appointing a party who has a substantial track record of successfully completing work of the type envisaged. This party should be the lead designer, responsible for promoting co-ordination and co-operation in the design work throughout the life of the project (see also ACoP para 79).

If the nature of work changes, appointments may need to be reconsidered.

Assessing competence and resources

The initial assessment of the various appointees' competence and resources with respect to health and safety issues should normally be part of a client's overall assessment of potential appointees. This may be delegated to a client's agent or advice may be sought from the planning supervisor.

> If a designer or contractor or other duty-holder is known to have undertaken successfully the relevant health and safety duties on similar projects, or can demonstrate this by providing references to recent similar work, then this will normally suffice as an initial assessment of competence and their ability to deploy the necessary resources.

Negotiations leading to the appointment of designers on more specialist work should include consideration of how to ensure and manage compliance with Regulation 13 (in which designers' duties are spelled out). Potential planning supervisors should be asked to explain how they propose to co-ordinate the work of the designers and ensure the generation of the pre-tender health and safety plan and the health and safety file.

Invitations for construction tenders can, on unusual or high-risk projects, call for outline method statements when the work to be done has implications for the integrity of the structure or impinges on a client's own operations. There may also be a request to indicate how the site will be made secure, organised and managed from the health and safety point of view. Care should be taken not to burden tendering contractors with excessive requirements.

Considerations affecting contract appointment may take account of:

- previous performance on similar projects
- explanation of how particular risks will be handled
- experience of key staff
- review of an outline construction health and safety plan prepared by the tenderer.

The manner in which assessments are undertaken should be appropriate to the client's prior knowledge of the organisation or person involved and the level of perceived risk on the project. Prior knowledge of the company will be a major consideration. Short questionnaires seeking details of experience and approach may suffice on low-risk projects, although any pre-appointment interview should generally include consideration of CDM-related issues. For higher-risk projects (such as work on an occupied site or involving deep excavations), the client should seek to build up a fuller picture of how a potential duty-holder will perform.

Under "term" or "partnership" contracts, a general assessment will normally be carried out of a contractor's competence and resources for the likely scope of work to be done. This form of contract will, therefore, be appropriate where emergency or fast-track work is envisaged. If especially risky or unusual projects are to be undertaken, a client should review the term contractor's capabilities for the job in question (see Chapter 9).

When assessing competence and resources, commercial factors are not directly relevant. However, further investigation is needed should the overall assessment of construction tenders show that (for example) the lowest bidder has significantly under-resourced his site establishment. Similarly, it will be a cause for concern if a planning supervisor to be appointed on a fixed-price fee basis puts in a low bid that allows little time for input during the construction phase of a project, when he has to liaise with the contractor's designers and ensure preparation of the health and safety file. Such concerns must be explored. Those who do not convince ought not to be appointed.

> Assessment of health and safety issues cannot be undertaken in isolation. It must be part of the overall assessment of tenderers. Health and safety are not add-ons.

Further information on the assessment of competence and resources is provided in Chapter 6. Clients should always ask their planning supervisor for advice where they are in any doubt.

1.2.8 Client's agent

See Section 1.2.2 for deciding whether to appoint an agent for the purposes of CDM.

Few clients will wish to appoint an independent adviser solely as client's agent, as this creates another interface for no advantage. The role can normally be assigned to a person or company already appointed by the client providing they satisfy the criteria of competence and adequate resources. There is no need or reason to separate health and safety from other management duties.

See Chapter 3 for details of the role, Chapter 6 concerning assessment of competence and resources and Chapter 9 concerning terms of appointment.

1.2.9 Designers

It is important to appreciate who are designers. Clearly the design team appointed by a client (or a design-and-build contractor) are designers. However, the ACoP (paras 109–111) makes it clear that in CDM the term "designer" has a broad meaning, including:

- those who analyse, calculate, do preparatory work, design, draw, specify, prepare bills of quantities
- those who arrange for their employees (or others under their control) so to do
- anyone who specifies or alters a design or who specifies the use of a particular method of work or material.

Nearly all participants may be designers, therefore, whether it be a client specifying a building layout or a type of construction or material, or a subcontractor deciding how he will do his work.

For a summary of a designer's duties under CDM see Section 4.4.1, or for more details refer to CIRIA C604. If a client wishes to act as a designer, criteria of competence and resources apply. If a planning supervisor or a designer believes that a client is making a design input, they should tell him that he is acquiring CDM duties and liabilities.

There is always a need to manage proper arrangements for design, particularly where there are contributions to be made by several designers. Someone should be appointed to that role and they will often (but not always) be named as "lead designer"; their role should include the promotion of co-ordination and co-operation of all throughout the life of a project. Designers must co-operate with the planning supervisor and other designers whether or not such an appointment is made (Reg 13(2)(c)).

See Chapter 6 concerning assessment of competence and resources and Chapter 9 concerning terms of appointment.

1.2.10 Planning supervisor

Because a planning supervisor's role is central to CDM and can entail a degree of involvement with all the other participants in a project, the client has to decide on a number of issues. For the sake of simplicity and accessibility, the key points are set out in question and answer form below.

Q. *Is it best to perform the role:*

- *in-house?*
- *by appointing an existing designer, project manager or contractor?*
- *by appointing an independent planning supervisor?*

A. There is no unique answer. The relevant issues have been outlined earlier in this section and clients will have to decide. Key points are:

- whoever undertakes the role should be competent and adequately resourced for the project. There is no other fundamental basis for judgement, from a CDM standpoint

- use of an independent planning supervisor is likely to cost a little more but may provide returns if they act as a facilitator and motivator of the other team members. There may be additional benefits to clients deriving from the planning supervisor's independence

- it may be deemed necessary to perform the role in-house at the early stages of a project (eg where there is commercial sensitivity). As a project progresses, others can then be given the role

- the appointment must be made once design decisions are being taken that will affect construction (normally, after feasibility and definition of the essential features of the project but while design decisions are still open to examination). If the work of a planning supervisor starts only after significant design decisions have been made, it is likely that they will not be revisited and that the pre-tender health and safety plan will be less effective than it ought to be.

Q. *Can a change of appointment be made as a project proceeds?*

A. The role of planning supervisor may be re-allocated, if the client so wishes, so long as the party undertaking the role at any time is competent and adequately resourced. Note that change introduces the risk of misunderstandings and must be carefully handled both in respect of contracts and day-to-day management. Two common reasons for transferring the role are:

- a client wishes to undertake the role during the early stages, later on transferring it to another party

- a client wishes to reduce the risk of contractual disputes during the construction phase (regardless of who has undertaken the duties pre-tender), by making the principal contractor responsible for planning supervision.

Q. *What are the main criteria to consider when tendering for, or negotiating with, a party to undertake the role of planning supervisor?*

A. The main criteria are:

- competence and resources, which must be adequate to the task ahead (see Chapter 6)
- cost, which is essentially a commercial matter; however, low-cost bids may suggest that inadequate resources will be available
- benefits the people involved would bring to the project through their skills and experience that are in addition to fulfilling their statutory duties. Examples include team-building (through the co-ordinating role) and contributing ideas to the project.

Q. *What are the key terms and conditions to be considered?*

A. The key terms and conditions are:

- exactly what is to be done and when as the project proceeds
- how the interfaces with the parties will work; note that back-to-back arrangements are desirable in the other parties' contracts and should include provision for access to the other parties, provision of information, attendance at meetings etc
- the reporting required by the client (or his representative) including matters to be decided by them
- how differences of opinion will be resolved including fall-back arrangements for dispute resolution.

Areas of concern are examined in Chapter 9 and also in CIRIA Publication C603 *CDM Regulations – practical guidance for planning supervisors*.

Note that the client will have to decide:

- who is to prepare the pre-tender health and safety plan
- who is to prepare, and then develop, the health and safety file
- whether the planning supervisor will be expected to advise the client on issues of competency and resource capabilities of prospective designers, principal contractors and/or other contractors
- whether the planning supervisor will be expected to advise the client on whether the principal contractor's construction health and safety plan has been sufficiently developed for the client to permit construction work to start.

There is no requirement in the Regulations for planning supervisors to monitor work on site. If a client requires a planning supervisor to undertake additional duties, such as monitoring work on site, then adequate contractual provision must be put in place.

Q. *Should the client monitor the work of his planning supervisor?*

A. This is not a duty imposed by the Regulations. However, a prudent client should not ignore clear evidence that things are not going well.

1.2.11 Principal contractor

The CDM Regulations create the (CDM) role of a principal contractor. The client or client's agent is responsible for ensuring that the party they appoint as principal contractor is competent and adequately resourced (from a CDM standpoint). In most cases this will be the main or managing contractor undertaking the works.

The ACoP states (para 80) that the principal contractor must be an organisation or individual who undertakes, carries out or manages construction work and notes that this will often be the main or managing contractor. It is not necessary to employ people who do site works to fall within the definition of contractor under CDM. Contract administrators and consultants may also undertake the principal contractor role, as may the planning supervisor – always subject to having the requisite competence and adequate resources. A client who is competent and adequately resourced can be a principal contractor.

On some projects where there is no main or managing contractor with a continuous presence on site, it is not immediately obvious who should be the principal contractor. Options include changing the party undertaking the role as the project proceeds, or charging one contractor to manage the site and take on duties as principal contractor. Alternatively, a client actively managing trade contractors may wish to undertake the role. Others involved in the project, such as the contract administrator or in some circumstances a consultant may be considered to be qualified, provided that the ACoP para 80 requirement is met.

Bearing in mind the extensive duties of the principal contractors that apply from start to finish of the construction phase and the need actively to manage the health and safety related activities of all contractors on site, the role should not be undertaken lightly. Before making any appointments, the client must be satisfied that those to be appointed are competent and adequately resourced.

1.2.12 Contractors

These appointments are normally likely to concern the client least. However, clients should consider putting in place contractual terms that require all contractors (whether appointed directly by the client, or indirectly) to provide their input to the health and safety file as early as possible and always before they leave site or receive full payment.

For further information on the role, see Chapter 3. For information on assessing competence and resources, see Chapter 6. For information on legal and contractual issues, see Chapter 9.

1.2.13 Interfaces

Interface issues arising from CDM need to be carefully managed. Ideally, each party will be represented for the purposes of CDM by a single named person who will be the prime point of contact, with an alternative as back-up. The client organisation is no exception in this respect.

Clear delegation will:

- avoid the risk of an accidental breakdown in communications
- provide a focal point for other parties to relate to
- provide a focus for CDM-related activities within the company
- ensure that decisions are promptly made and all instructions and communications are ratified.

At the end of the project, management of the health and safety file will be an ongoing client responsibility, which must be clearly recognised, allocated and resourced.

1.2.14   Providing information

Under CDM, clients have to provide information about the site and its neighbourhood. It is not good practice to expect tendering contractors to assess issues such as contaminated land, or unstable structures or asbestos. Surveys should not be withheld on the grounds that to provide them may open the client to liability. Contractual disclaimers can be made – but the information must not be withheld. The detail of surveys that are required will be a matter of judgement and common sense. If a particularly price-sensitive issue is involved (such as contamination, the risks of which cannot be fully assessed until work is well under way) sensible forms of contract (for example based on declared schedules of rates) should be used rather than forcing a contractor to guess. Otherwise the contractor may be inadequately resourced to undertake the work safely or, alternatively, he may overprice his work in anticipation of a worst-scenario outcome.

1.2.15   Providing adequate time

The importance of time as a resource is discussed in Section 6.2.3. The prime responsibility for setting the programme for a project rests with the clients. In order for the CDM duty-holders to manage hazard and risk competently, they will need both relevant information and time to consider the hazards and risks both individually and as a team. Early appointment of the duty-holders will assist, including the involvement of contractors during the pre-construction design stages.

1.2.16   Health and safety plan

A client need have little contact with a health and safety plan at pre-tender stage, although he will make inputs by providing information and making provision for interfaces between the contractor and his own undertaking, for example ensuring that his own site rules are included. At construction stage, the only contact required is to ensure that no work starts on site until a principal contractor's construction health and safety plan is adequately developed for that purpose. A client may also need to respond to events as they arise, including disputes between people they have appointed and following health and safety incidents.

1.2.17   Health and safety file

A health and safety file is a significant document to be delivered to the client at the end of a project and is examined in Chapter 8. Clients should note that:

- their requirements for the file should be clearly expressed to whoever is to prepare it, before they start work. The client must appoint someone to prepare the file; this will normally be the planning supervisor, or the principal contractor, or the lead designer. In the latter cases, the planning supervisor must have a role in its completion so that he can meet his obligations under the Regulations concerning the file.

- arrangements for holding it, updating it and making it available must be thought through and put in place. The health and safety file is a recent feature, but it will increasingly be seen as a structure's log book and an asset to hold and use in the future. It will provide much of the information that a client must provide for future work, without repeating earlier work that has already been paid for.

1.2.18	**Motivation**

Although a client has no duty under CDM to promote safety on his site, some clients will wish to take the lead in encouraging safety on their sites. The principal contractor must fully co-ordinate activities of this type.

1.2.19	**Avoiding and resolving disputes**

Inevitably, CDM may give rise to disputes in which a party's commercial interests are at risk. For example, if a principal contractor's construction health and safety plan is rejected as not being sufficiently developed, the start of work on site may be delayed. Overhead costs rise, subcontracts are at risk, the project completion date is at risk and there may be other contractual issues. This problem can be lessened by allowing sufficient time in the contract programme for the health and safety plan to be prepared and agreed, and by maintaining close liaison during this critical period. It cannot be solved by taking a risk and allowing construction to start, as this lays a client open to both criminal prosecution and civil action. If the construction health and safety plan is unsatisfactory to the client or his agent, this should immediately be noted in writing to the principal contractor, with an explanation. His response should be carefully listened to and immediately recorded and responded to, again in writing, and so on. Positive management of a problem will help to reduce misunderstandings and reduce its impact. For further information about the construction health and safety plan, see Chapter 7.

If contractors have to change their methods of safe working in response to health and safety issues that only become apparent after the construction contract is signed, a claim may arise for an extension of time and/or extra monies, on the basis that the pre-tender health and safety plan was inadequate. Under some forms of contract, there may be specific provision for such monies to be paid in certain circumstances. Most forms will state that there is no such ground or be silent. This is a question of where provision for the risk of this type of contingency should best lie. For most work the risk will best lie with contractors, because they are in control on site. There may be disputes between the principal contractor and contractors in this respect, as well as disputes involving the client. So far such disputes have not been common.

The CDM Regulations set out to improve co-ordination. Inevitably this will sometimes entail activities that are viewed as interfering with the freedom of some participants, design co-ordination being one example. It is recommended that clients should insert contract terms to ensure that all concerned give the planning supervisor access, provide information and recognise the CDM duties of all parties. If not, disputes that arise may not be resolved easily (see Chapter 9).

A procedure for resolving disputes should be written into all contracts; adjudication procedures now have to be included in all contracts (Housing Grants, Construction and Regeneration Act 1996).

2   When and how do the Regulations apply?

2.1   WHEN DO THE REGULATIONS APPLY?

2.1.1   Introduction

This section explains when and to what extent the Regulations apply. Be aware that "notification" is a separate matter, although work that is notifiable will always be within the scope of CDM. Notification is covered in Section 2.2.

The extent to which the Regulations apply varies, depending on the scale and type of any project that will involve "construction work" (this term is explained in Section 2.1.3).

For most construction projects a client will have various duties including the duty to appoint a planning supervisor and a principal contractor for each project. The client's duties are discussed fully in Chapter 3.

A client can call on his designers to explain his duties under CDM, which may include advice on whether the Regulations apply and, if so, to what extent.

Full definitions of the terms used in this chapter are given in the Glossary.

2.1.2   Application

The extent to which CDM applies varies according to the nature of a project that will involve "construction work", and whether responsibility for enforcement of health and safety legislation rests with the Health and Safety Executive or with a local authority environmental health department. The HSE will be the enforcing authority for all but a very few construction projects.

If the project is "notifiable" all parts of the Regulations apply, whatever the nature of the work or the number of people who are engaged in "construction work".

If the project involves demolition or dismantling of a structure, **or** can reasonably be expected to involve five or more people engaged in "construction work" **at any time**, all the Regulations apply, with the possible exception of that relating to notification.

The client has the same duties on these projects whether or not the project is "notifiable". He will need to appoint a planning supervisor and principal contractor, and to fulfil the other responsibilities set out in Chapter 3.

The guidance in Chapter 3 onwards is relevant to projects where the client's duties apply.

> The client's duties will apply to all but the most minor construction projects.

The client has no CDM duties in relation to minor short-duration projects that do not involve demolition or dismantling and where the maximum number of people likely to be engaged in construction work at any time can reasonably be expected to be fewer than five. On such projects only the designer has duties under CDM.

The "test" is what the client should reasonably expect. It is bad practice, and often illegal, for a client to impose very tight programmes or to limit the number of days of work to be done and the maximum number of people on site simply in an attempt to avoid having CDM duties. The importance of time as a resource also needs to be borne in mind and is discussed in Section 6.2.3.

If the local authority environmental health department is the enforcing authority for the project, none of the requirements of CDM applies – but this is rarely the case.

> A flow diagram showing how CDM applies is shown as Figure 1 on p 5 of the ACoP, reproduced in this guide as Figure 1, on p 31.

2.1.3   What is construction work?

Construction work means most building, civil engineering construction work, repair and maintenance. A full definition of construction work (see Glossary) is given in the Regulations and discussed in the ACoP (paras 26–29). It may be generally described as:

- virtually any work on a "structure" (see Section 2.1.4)
- preparatory work or investigations of a physical nature
- demolition or dismantling
- virtually any work on services fixed to a structure.

Therefore a great many tasks in the world of building, civil engineering, property management, manufacturing and process industries constitute "construction work". New-build, maintenance, renovation and conversion may all be in the scope of the definition. Activities such as the installation of telecommunications or computer services within a building might not generally be regarded as construction work, but fall within the definition.

Even where the particular requirements of CDM do not apply, other requirements to manage hazard and risk remain, under other health and safety legislation.

2.1.4   What is a structure?

The Regulations give a full definition of the word "structure" (see Glossary). The word has a wide-ranging meaning and includes:

- any building
- any other form of construction work, such as infrastructure work
- temporary works
- scaffolding
- fixed plant.

2.1.5 Exclusions

There are some specific exclusions (see Sections 2.1.6–2.1.13):

- day-to-day cleaning work
- works for domestic clients
- works for which the local authority is the enforcing authority
- work solely on fixed plant where there is no risk of falling more than 2 m
- site survey (but not site exploration or site investigation)
- certain work associated with extraction of mineral resources
- work off-site.

See also Section 2.1.13.

2.1.6 Cleaning work

Designers have to consider how future cleaning work as defined (see Glossary) can be carried out safely where there is a risk of falling more than 2 m, and appropriate methods designed-in (such as anchor points etc).

The execution of day-to-day cleaning is not within the scope of CDM, but special work that involves cleaning with high-pressure water or corrosive chemicals is included in the definition of construction work, and CDM may apply.

A client's only duty when commissioning cleaning work as defined, is to make available relevant information from the health and safety file.

2.1.7 Work for domestic clients

Domestic clients have no duties under the Regulations, except where the work is being done by a developer on their behalf. The term "developer" includes any company or individual carrying out construction that will become a residence, such as a builder/developer or a housing association. The developer's role is discussed further in Chapter 3. Note that work on rented domestic premises is **not** excluded from the Regulations.

2.1.8 Local authority as enforcing authority

Where a local authority is the enforcing authority, CDM does not apply. The role of local authorities as enforcing authority applies **only** to certain limited categories of buildings, such as offices, shops and warehouses and **only** for minor construction works which meet **ALL** the following criteria:

- not notifiable under CDM (see below)
- carried out in an area that is entirely internal (ie inside a building)
- normal activities are not suspended
- the contractor will not have the right to exclude persons from the area of the works.

The detailed Regulations are complex and clients should, if in doubt, apply CDM (a safe solution) or consult with an expert on health and safety law.

2.1.9   **Work on fixed plant with safe access**

"Fixed plant" is defined in the Glossary. The Regulations apply to any fixed plant "in respect of work which is installation, commissioning, de-commissioning or dismantling and where any such work involves a risk of a person falling more than 2 metres". However, if the work is part of a larger project to which CDM applies, then it will itself be within scope.

2.1.10   **Site survey, exploration and investigation**

"Construction work" does not include site survey, but does include site exploration or site investigation.

These terms are not defined, but it is recommended that clients consider any operations involving excavation, drilling, boring or other disruptive activity as "construction work".

Many site exploration and investigation activities will themselves be construction projects often imposing CDM duties on the client and others. An example of this would be a geotechnical investigation involving machinery, where five or more people will be on site. The client would normally be expected to procure information from such an investigation and make it available to those involved in subsequent projects relating to the site.

2.1.11   **Mineral extraction**

Regulation 2(1) states that construction work does not include "the exploration for or extraction of mineral resources or activities preparatory thereto carried out at a place where such exploration or extraction is carried out". However, the Regulations do cover above-ground construction work (such as building work or the installation of machinery).

Site exploration or site preparation or the construction of boreholes for water extraction does not constitute mineral extraction.

2.1.12   **Work off-site**

The ACoP (para 27) explains that the Regulations do not apply to work in factories or off-site workshops.

2.1.13   **Other exclusions**

The ACoP (para 27) also lists the following work as being outside the scope of CDM:

- relocation of marquees and tents
- maintenance of fixed plant, *other* than services
- tree-planting and horticultural work (see also Section 2.1.18)
- archaeological investigations (see also Section 2.1.17)
- positioning and removal of lightweight partitions (offices, exhibitions)
- scaffolding for support or access in non-construction work (see also Section 2.1.19)
- surveying, including taking levels and measurements and examining structures
- ships and mobile offshore installations (see also Section 2.1.20)
- fabrication of elements for offshore installations.

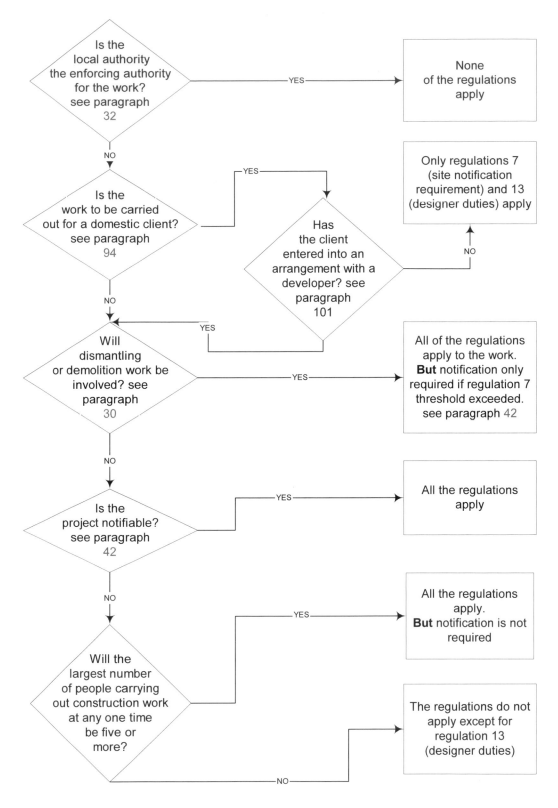

Figure I   *The application of CDM (taken from Figure 1 "Where CDM applies" in the ACoP).*
Note: the paragraphs referred to are those in the ACoP

2.1.14 Demolition and dismantling

The ACoP (para 30) advises that "demolition and dismantling" includes work in which a structure or a substantial portion of a structure is deliberately pulled down, destroyed or taken apart (whether for reuse or not).

HSE advice is that the striking or taking down of a scaffold structure or other similar temporary works is not considered to be demolition and dismantling. (See also Section 2.1.19.)

All demolition and dismantling work is subject to the CDM Regulations.

2.1.15 Maintenance

Maintenance of a structure is clearly within the scope of CDM if it meets the criteria for application of CDM.

Maintenance of fixed plant will not generally constitute "construction work" unless it is carried out as part of a wider project, for example involving maintenance of associated services. However, some major items of plant may themselves be "structures" within the meaning of CDM, or be supported by "structures". If in doubt, CDM should be applied.

2.1.16 Term maintenance

Individual projects within a term contract that in themselves meet the criteria for application fall within the scope of CDM. Whether individual tasks should be combined to form a CDM project is a matter of common sense. For example:

- if a large team is working together on a building refurbishment for two months, that is a project where CDM will apply
- if a small team is moving around, doing day-to-day maintenance in or on a structure, CDM would not apply, except for designers' duties.

Regardless of whether or not CDM strictly applies, it may be sensible to apply the same management systems to all the work. This would not be a statutory obligation.

2.1.17 Archaeology

Many building projects involve archaeological investigations and/or an ongoing watching brief, or both. The scope of CDM does not include archaeological investigations (see also ACoP para 27). If the work is part of a construction project, however, it will be within the scope of construction work and some or all of the requirements of CDM may apply. See also Section 2.1.21 Mixed projects.

2.1.18 Landscaping

Landscaping does not appear in the CDM list of construction activities but some landscaping operations may be within the scope of CDM if they involve construction work (such as drainage, major earthworks or stabilisation of a slope) or where landscaping forms part of a larger construction project. The ACoP (para 27) excludes "tree planting and general horticultural work" from the scope of CDM, but where such work is undertaken in potentially hazardous situations, applying the principles of CDM may be an appropriate means of ensuring that the risks are effectively managed.

2.1.19 Scaffolding

The erection and taking down of scaffolding used for the purpose of construction is construction work (see also Section 2.1.13). The ACoP (para 27) advises that work on scaffolding for other purposes is not in the scope of CDM.

2.1.20 Offshore installations

Fixed offshore installations within UK territorial waters (eg windfarms) are covered by CDM (see ACoP para 41), unlike mobile installations (see Section 2.1.13).

2.1.21 Mixed projects

The ACoP (para 28) notes that where projects include both work that is within the scope of CDM and some that is not, the overlap should be addressed in the health and safety plan. It would be sensible to manage all work to the standards of CDM, to reduce risks and uncertainty.

2.1.22 Insurance

The HSE has advised that, when work is carried out that will be paid for by an insurance claim, the client is the party who arranges for the work to be done, ie appoints designers and contractors. If a domestic client arranges for work to be done, CDM does not apply. If an insurance company takes on these tasks on behalf of a domestic client, the insurance company is the client and the exemption for domestic clients does not apply. The ACoP (paras 97–100) also notes that agents of insurance companies and providers of warranties who arrange for remedial work are the clients for the work and the exemption does not apply.

2.1.23 The "four people on site" rule

Where the maximum number of people engaged in construction work at any time can reasonably be expected to exceed four, all the Regulations will apply (see Section 2.1.2).

There is some doubt as to who should be counted as being engaged in construction work, but case law indicates that people undertaking ancillary activities such as supervision of construction work should probably be included. If in doubt, clients should assume that they have duties under CDM.

2.1.24 Designers' duties

Designers have duties in relation to all construction projects, *regardless* of whether or not CDM imposes duties on the client.

2.2 WHEN DOES THE HSE HAVE TO BE NOTIFIED?

2.2.1 What is notification?

Notification is the act of informing the HSE that a project is to be carried out, so that they are aware of it and have the opportunity of visiting the project or the participating parties if they wish.

Note that if a client appoints a client's agent to act on his behalf, this may be declared to the HSE (see Chapter 6). This is a separate matter from notification.

2.2.2   **Which projects are notifiable?**

Regulation 2 defines what a notifiable project is. In essence, a project will be notifiable if the client (and their planning supervisor) can reasonably expect that the construction work will:

- last more than 30 days (the 30 days rule) from when it starts **or**
- will involve more than 500 person-days (the 500 person-days rule).

There are no other "tests" for deciding which projects are notifiable.

A client's CDM duties may apply to projects that are not notifiable.

The 30 days rule and the 500 person-days rule are examined below.

A client must not confuse notification with application (see Section 2.1).

2.2.3   **Who should notify and when?**

A client has no duty in respect of notification. If a project is notifiable, the planning supervisor should notify the HSE as soon as he is appointed.

2.2.4   **The 30 days rule**

The ACoP (para 43) defines the 30 days in terms of being 30 working days where a working day is any day on which any construction work is carried out.

2.2.5   **The 500 person-days rule**

This rule is designed to pick up heavily manned projects which, although of short duration, would be likely to suffer from interface problems and time pressures. The ACoP (para 43) defines total "person-days" as the total number of shifts worked by everyone in the project, including supervisors. It advises that, in borderline cases, it is best to notify HSE.

2.3   **INTERPRETATION**

2.3.1   **Start of a project**

A project starts (for the purposes of CDM) when a client has decided to proceed beyond feasibility studies and when decisions are about to be made that could have health and safety implications during subsequent construction work or cleaning work. It is necessary to appoint the planning supervisor at about the same time as the designers start concept design; at that point, there should be sufficient knowledge about the project to determine the competence required of the planning supervisor.

Note:

- certain early activities may themselves form projects for the purposes of CDM, such as significant site investigations or enabling works such as demolition or removal of asbestos-containing materials

- financial sanction alone cannot be used to determine when a project starts. This is because financial sanction may not be obtained until shortly before construction starts, by which time the key decisions will have been made

- the ACoP (para 75) emphasises the importance of appointing the planning supervisor at the earliest stage of design, ie concept; "planning supervisors must be appointed at or before the start of design work".

2.3.2   Changing circumstances

If a project increases in scope or if other significant changes occur (for example, it is decided to demolish a structure) so that the outstanding work will be within the scope of CDM, the Regulations should be applied.

Steps must be taken immediately to put appropriate measures in place (appoint a planning supervisor and a principal contractor, prepare a health and safety plan etc).

On the other hand, if a small project unexpectedly runs over 30 days by a few days, there may be no benefit in applying CDM. The important test is whether as a result of applying CDM health and safety hazards would be better managed.

2.3.3   Making decisions

A client has to make the following crucial decisions, the outcome of which should be recorded:

- whether the CDM Regulations apply

- whether to appoint a client's agent

- how to manage the appointment of designer(s), planning supervisor, principal contractor and contractor(s)

- whether to permit work to start on site.

It is bad practice to avoid applying CDM by splitting a project into a number of contracts and arguing that each contract is a small project to which CDM does not apply. In the event of an accident, were investigations to show that such tactics had been used, they could be interpreted as a material breach of the Regulations. Action may be instigated against the client under other legislation, or in civil proceedings. Any savings on CDM-related work may in any event be negated by the additional costs arising from letting and managing separate contracts.

> It is good practice for clients to err on the side of caution when deciding if CDM applies, particularly if there are significant health and safety risks to be managed.

3 Who is a client and what is a client's agent?

3.1 THE REGULATIONS

3.1.1 Definitions

The Regulations define a "client" as a "person for whom a project is carried out, whether it is carried out by another person or is carried out in-house". A "person" may be an individual, a company or a corporate identity – which includes an organisation such as a local authority. For construction work, the client will usually be a company or organisation, but may be an individual. A person acting on behalf of a company or organisation is not the person defined by the Regulations; the duty-holder in such situations is the company or organisation, not the employee.

The Regulations define a client's agent for the purposes of CDM as a person who acts as if he were the client. Such an appointment may be either:

- declared to the HSE by the client's agent, in which case CDM will apply to the client's agent as if he were the client, or
- undeclared, in which case CDM will apply to both the client and his agent.

The extent to which clients remain responsible for ensuring that their duties are properly executed may be a matter of contention, but the declaration to the HSE that a competent and adequately resourced client's agent has been appointed may provide some measure of protection to a client.

Clients may decide to appoint an adviser who will assist in carrying out the client's role, but unless a client's agent appointment has been made and declared to the HSE, clients will be expected to be in control of their CDM duties.

> The use of the term "client's agent" for the purposes of CDM carries with it statutory responsibilities and should not be confused with the use of the term generally.
>
> **In this guide, the term "client's agent" refers to a client's agent for the purposes of CDM.**

When it is not immediately apparent to the parties involved in a project with several stakeholders exactly who the client is for the purposes of CDM, they should decide who will take on the client's duties. That party will then carry out the client's duties on behalf of the stakeholders, ie he will be their client's agent. Such arrangements should be explicit and recorded.

3.1.2 Developers

All developers are clients under CDM. However, Regulation 5 recognises and legislates for a particular category of developer, which is called "the developer". The ACoP (paras 101, 102) states that this category of developer arises when commercial developers sell domestic premises before a project is complete.

The developer, as defined, includes housing associations, self-build companies and other such bodies who may be profit-making or non-profit-making. The effect of this requirement (Regulation 5) is to close the loophole by which such developers could claim that CDM does not apply because the client for the purposes of CDM is not themselves, but their domestic customers, and that the CDM exemption of domestic clients therefore applies.

3.1.3 Competence of a client's agent

The Regulations and ACoP require clients to take reasonable steps to assess the competence of a prospective client's agent. An appropriate response is, therefore, to ask for reassurance from those being considered for the role of client's agent whether:

- they are capable of performing the role of client's agent
- this can be demonstrated to the client, with reference to their training, qualifications, experience and skills.

3.1.4 Role of a client's agent

Once a client's agent has declared himself as such to the HSE, he has the statutory duty to carry out the client's obligations under the Regulations and the HSE will relate to him as if he were the client. There are three crucial tasks that relate particularly to CDM.

1 Providing health and safety-related information for designers.

2 Appointments of designers, planning supervisor and principal contractor.

3 Permitting the construction phase to start.

These critical decisions affect projects as a whole and can lead to clients incurring substantial costs. It follows that any agent's appointment must make plain the scope of his authority.

The longer-term role of holding and making available a health and safety file is likely to revert to the client once construction has been completed; this requires clarification under the terms of appointment of the client's agent.

Throughout this guide, duties that are the client's may be transferred to a client's agent, under his terms of appointment.

The terms of appointment of a client's agent should be in writing and include:

- the duties
- the duration of the appointment
- the requirement for formal declaration to the HSE
- provision of the necessary powers to perform the duties.

3.2 THE ROLE OF A CLIENT IN MANAGING HAZARD AND RISK

3.2.1 The client's role

As prime mover for a project, the client has a key role in ensuring that construction hazards and risks are managed competently, by:

- ensuring that projects are properly managed throughout
- timely appointment of competent CDM duty-holders
- ensuring they have the resources and time to do their work
- providing the information they need
- setting in place contractual arrangements that make it clear who does what on the project and that provide mechanisms to ensure they co-operate and co-ordinate their work
- ensuring that a safe environment is maintained for the client's employees, the public and other third parties

> Above all, a client should provide leadership that demonstrates by action that health and safety is top of the agenda.

Note that the ACoP (para 16) clearly states that the arrangements which a client makes for CDM need to be set out in written form in all but the simplest situations.

3.2.2 Benefits to the client

The benefits to a client from the effective implementation of CDM are outlined in the ACoP para 54 and are:

- improved planning and control
- reduced likelihood of unforeseen problems, delays and cost overruns
- reduced cost in operation (bearing in mind the fact that operation costs much more than construction)
- reduced accidents and ill-health, with all that is entailed, including delays and bad publicity.

3.3 EXAMPLES

3.3.1 Joint venture

Three pharmaceutical companies set up a joint venture to manufacture a new product. The production facility will be at one of the participant's sites and that participant will procure the new works before a new operational team is recruited.

The question arose as to who was the client. The joint venture was strictly the client, initially a shell company with no resources. It was decided that the company on whose site the works would be situated would take on the client's responsibilities, ie act as client's agent and declare this appointment as such to the HSE.

3.3.2 The new client

Two sisters decided to build a small nursery school in their village. For the purposes of CDM, the sisters were jointly the client. Their architect explained CDM and they decided to appoint him as a client's agent; he prepared a letter of appointment for their signature and he declared to the HSE that he was the agent. The architect thereby became the declared agent with full responsibility for all the client's duties.

3.3.3 Client's representative

An airline company appointed a firm of quantity surveyors to act on its behalf in the procurement of a new airside staff facility, naming the firm as "client's representative". The firm in turn appointed designers to prepare a technical brief for a design-and-build contract. The designers wrote to the airline company, informing it of its CDM duties as client. The airline company wrote to the client's representative, asking the firm to deal with the matter on its behalf. The client's representative had been given authority and accepted the duty of acting on behalf of the client in full, up to the time the facility and its health and safety file were handed to the client. The fact that there was no formal appointment of a client's agent declared to the HSE meant that, in the event of a problem arising, the HSE would look to the client for information and explanations.

This could have been avoided by making a formal appointment and by ensuring that the client's agent made a declaration to the HSE.

> The term "client's representative" commonly used in the construction industry is not recognised under CDM. It is not a synonym for client's agent for the purposes of CDM.

3.3.4 Tenants

Having rented a factory unit, a company making electrical goods decided to rewire the entire store so that they could set up and display on stands anywhere in the store, dropping electrics from a grid of sockets in the ceiling. Because there would be more than four construction workers on site, CDM applied.

The client for the work was the tenant. A consultant was appointed to act as project manager, planning supervisor and declared client's agent for the duration of the project.

3.3.5 Utilities

As part of a project, a property developer client placed an order with a water company to install a new water supply to the site, with a meter chamber located on the site. The water company contracted-out the work. The developer client was unsure whether he or the utility was the client for this work and was unclear how the contractor doing the job related to him and to his principal contractor.

This type of situation, where there is potentially more than one client's project on a site at the same time, requires common sense and goodwill to resolve. The parties involved need to come to an understanding that meets properly the statutory requirements of CDM and other health and safety legislation. The ACoP (para 40) provides further guidance. In this case, the water company acted as client for the specialist work but required that the principal contractor for the main works co-ordinated (with respect to health and safety) their contractor's work on the property developer's site.

> Where utilities are involved, a clear allocation of duties under CDM is essential.

3.3.6   PFI project

A government agency wished to promote a PFI (private finance initiative) project on a site it had procured. It was advised that, until a contract was signed with an operating company, the agency was the client for the purposes of CDM, as per para 69 of the ACoP. The agency's project manager carried out the client function until the concession contract was signed. The agency procured and freely provided information and instructed each of the bidding consortia that it would have to appoint a planning supervisor for their scheme. Once the concession contract was signed, the agency's project manager informed the successful consortium that it was now the client as it had control of the site and all construction works on it for the agreed period of 25 years.

PFI projects can become very complex. It is important that the client's CDM role is clearly allocated and, if necessary, changed as effective ownership changes. It was good practice for the government agency to set out at the start how this was to be handled throughout the life of the project.

> Under PFI or similar situations it is necessary formally to decide who is the client and who is carrying out the other CDM roles at any time.

4 Roles and responsibilities

4.1 THE PARTIES TO CDM

4.1.1 Who are the parties to CDM?

The named roles are:

- client
- client's agent
- designer(s)
- planning supervisor
- principal contractor
- contractor(s).

The decision whether to appoint a client's agent is reviewed in Chapter 1.

The indicative relationship of the parties on typical projects is shown in Figure 2 on p 46.

4.1.2 How do the parties relate to each other?

Every project will have its own characteristics, and clients will need to decide exactly how they are going to set up their projects so that CDM tasks are undertaken properly and economically.

The relationship between the parties is founded upon their duties under the Regulations; they each have duties to fulfil and success relies upon each party performing their duties in a proper manner. How they relate will depend upon their contracts and the way in which certain tasks are assigned – particularly tasks relating to the creation of the health and safety plan and the health and safety file.

The duties of the planning supervisor and the principal contractor are both co-ordinating roles relating to the planning of health and safety issues during design and construction respectively. These roles must meld with the formal contractual roles and maintain the authority of the project manager.

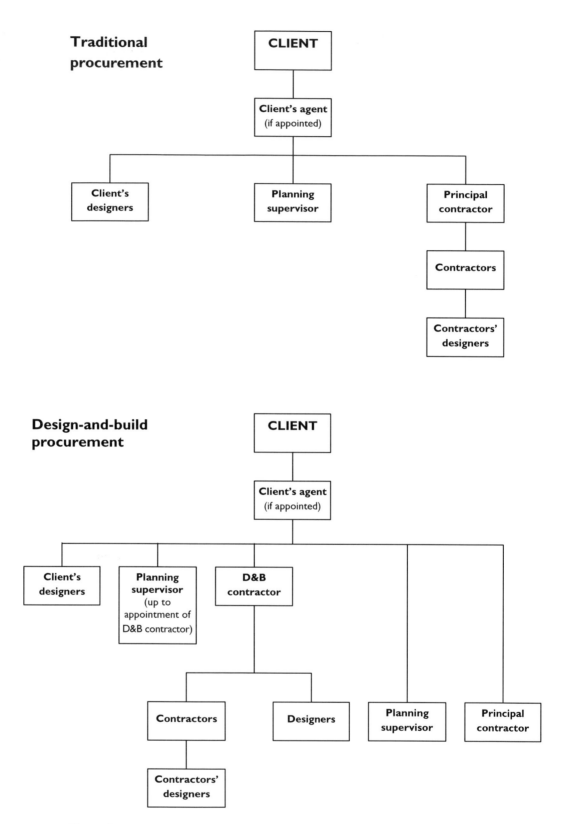

Figure 2 *How CDM duty-holders relate to a client*

Notes

(1) This figure shows possible examples of the direct CDM relationship of appointment of the parties to the client. There are other relationships, some of which may cut across contractual boundaries and the administrative links necessary for this to happen should be provided for in the various contracts.

(2) There is no reason why roles should not be combined eg one of the designers acting as planning supervisor (etc).

(3) The main or design-and-build contractor will normally be the principal contractor.

(4) The planning supervisor in design-and-build procurement may be within the design-and-build contractor's organisation or may be an independent appointment.

4.2 CLIENT'S DUTIES

4.2.1 Introduction

Until CDM, clients were not explicitly charged under statute with duties relating to health and safety in construction, although implicit duties existed under the Health and Safety at Work etc Act 1974. The CDM Regulations emphasise that clients have a key role.

4.2.2 Making appointments

As well as appointing designers and contractors, clients must appoint a planning supervisor and a principal contractor where CDM applies to a project. These appointments may be made to competent parties who are already involved in the project. This could simplify matters and reduce costs.

Before making an appointment a client must be reasonably satisfied that the organisation or individual concerned has adequate competence and resources relating to health and safety. How this can be judged is examined in Chapter 6.

4.2.3 Providing information

Information that a client has or could reasonably be expected to have or to obtain about the existing site must be made available to the planning supervisor. See Section 5.2.2 for further information.

A client may delegate tasks for the acquisition or confirmation of information. However, the client should check that such arrangements have been effectively discharged.

4.2.4 Allowing work to start on site

It is a client's duty under Regulation 10, as explained in ACoP para 87, to allow a principal contractor sufficient time to develop the project's health and safety plan before starting construction (see Chapter 7).

A client must not permit contractors to start work on site until the construction health and safety plan has been sufficiently developed (ie it covers the basic procedures and arrangements for site organisation, site rules, emergency procedures, welfare provisions etc and the specific measures to be taken to manage the early work elements such as site clearance, demolition, earthworks etc). The judgement should be based upon what is reasonable at the time and the degree to which the design is developed. A more developed plan (in terms of methods of work and co-ordination of activities) should be in place for higher-risk activities such as demolition. Clients often rely upon the advice of their planning supervisor as to whether the health and safety plan proffered by the principal contractor is adequate to allow them to permit construction to start. The ACoP gives advice on these matters in paras 88 and 233–239.

4.2.5 Holding the health and safety file and making it available

When a project is handed to the client, normally at the end of the construction phase, the planning supervisor will ensure that the health and safety file is passed to the client. For as long as he has control of the structure, the client has to hold this file and make it available to anyone who needs to see it to arrange or carry out future construction work (including maintenance) and cleaning work (see Section 2.1.6). This duty is of particular note because it has no time limitation once the file is in the client's hands.

Note that the strict requirement is that each "structure" should have a health and safety file. The way in which a large project is divided into "structures", possibly with separate health and safety files, should be decided at an early stage. If left undecided, there will be delay and additional costs as information is reformatted.

The health and safety file (or the relevant parts of it) will need to be made available to leaseholders or purchasers of the structure (or parts of it). This requirement may be met by providing copies of relevant sections of the health and safety file to tenants or leaseholders, the owner continuing to hold and update the health and safety file and to distribute amendments to other holders.

Further information about the health and safety file is given in Chapter 8.

4.2.6 Other roles

Clients may decide to undertake other roles, but only if they are suitably competent and resourced. This could include being:

- designer
- planning supervisor
- principal contractor
- contractor.

Clients should be aware that if they make an input to design (for example by setting standards or imposing methods of construction) they become a designer for the purposes of CDM and the designer's duties under CDM then apply to them.

4.3 A CLIENT'S RESPONSE

4.3.1 Organisation

Clear decisions should be made about:

- whether CDM applies
- whether a client's agent (or other advice/assistance) is required
- what appointments need to be made and when to make them
- allocating tasks and resolving the interfaces between the appointees (see Section 9.2) terms of appointment
- gathering information (see Section 5.2.2) and making it available to the planning supervisor
- the structure of the health and safety file
- allowing construction to start
- holding and making available health and safety file(s).

Particular care is needed to ensure that the responsibility for holding and making available the file is clearly assigned within a client's organisation.

4.3.2 Procedures

Having decided how to organise CDM activities, clients should consider putting in place simple procedures so that the tasks are carried out in a consistent and reliable manner. The documentation of a client's requirements is required by the ACoP (para 16).

4.4   OTHER PARTIES' DUTIES (IN BRIEF)

4.4.1   Designers

Designers have to:

- check that their clients are aware of their duties under CDM
- seek to eliminate or reduce hazards and risks in their design
- co-operate with the planning supervisor and other designers
- provide information for the pre-tender health and safety plan and health and safety file.

Note that the term "designer" includes all those who make decisions about the design of and planning for construction work, including temporary works designers (see Glossary).

4.4.2   Planning supervisor

Planning supervisors have to:

- notify the HSE about the project
- advise on competence and resources of other parties, when asked
- co-ordinate the work of all designers with respect to health and safety, taking reasonable steps to check that they co-operate and comply with their duties until all design work is completed
- ensure that the pre-tender health and safety plan is prepared and provided to contractors
- be in a position to advise the client when the construction plan is adequately developed to permit work to start on site
- ensure that a health and safety file is prepared and passed to the client when the construction work is complete.

4.4.3   Principal contractor

Principal contractors have to:

- prepare, develop and implement the construction health and safety plan
- co-operate with the planning supervisor
- co-ordinate and direct the handling of health and safety issues by all the contractors on site, including the enforcement of any written site rules
- appoint only competent and adequately resourced contractors
- provide the planning supervisor with access to their own designers and the designers of other contractors
- limit access to the site to authorised persons
- ensure that contractors' employees are informed, trained and consulted about health and safety
- display the HSE notification on site and ensure that people on site are aware of the site rules
- supply and co-operate in the collection of information for the health and safety file.

4.4.4   Contractors

Contractors have to:

- co-operate with the principal contractor and comply with his CDM directions
- comply with rules stated in the health and safety plan
- provide health and safety information, including risk assessments, to the principal contractor
- provide information for the health and safety plan and health and safety file to the principal contractor
- inform their employees, and ensure they are aware of and have access to relevant parts of the construction health and safety plan
- appoint only competent, adequately resourced subcontractors (including designers)
- inform the principal contractor should there be a reportable event, within the meaning of the Reporting of Injuries, Diseases and Dangerous Occurrences Regulations (RIDDOR)
- co-operate with the planning supervisor if design is carried out by that contractor or by that contractor's subcontractors.

4.4.5   Health and Safety Executive

The Health and Safety Executive has powers to secure compliance with health and safety law and to ensure that health and safety risks are managed and controlled. Their activities include:

- giving advice (see Section 1.2.2)
- visiting construction sites and design offices
- inspecting the work and procedures of the parties involved
- investigating accidents and incidents
- issuing improvement or prohibition notices where they judge there are shortfalls in CDM or other health and safety provisions
- prosecuting organisations and individuals.

5   The phases of a construction project

5.1   PLANNING

5.1.1   Inception activities

Activities during the inception phase may include:

- feasibility studies
- site surveys
- the preparation of project briefs
- outline/planning consultation
- statutory processes and procedures.

Inception activities that occur before a client decides to proceed with a project are not within the formal scope of CDM. However, designers involved in these activities need to consider health and safety hazards and risks when weighing up options because CDM will apply if the project proceeds and consideration of these matters at a later time may invalidate the earlier work.

5.1.2   Strategy for compliance

CDM applies to a project, not a contract; there may be several contracts to execute a project. The client needs to decide how CDM is to be handled throughout the project as part of deciding how to procure the project. The strategy for making appointments, the scope of each appointment and the contractual framework should be decided before design starts. It is crucial to clients that terms of appointment are aligned with project administration and respect the authority of the project manager.

5.1.3   Start of a project

Once a client has an intention to construct, his first step is normally to appoint a lead designer who will address or devise the brief and start to devise concept designs. This is when the Regulations come into play. If CDM applies, the client must also appoint a planning supervisor as soon as concept design starts – see Section 2.3.1.

> Lack of full and final financial sanction by the client is not a reason for failing to operate or postponing the introduction of CDM. It is the decision to progress beyond feasibility studies that triggers CDM because it demonstrates a reasonable intention to construct.

5.1.4   Project programme

Noting the importance of time as a resource (see Section 6.2.3), it is vital that the client's programme recognises the need for CDM duty-holders to be appointed as early as possible and to have time to perform their duties in a proper manner.

5.1.5   **Project budget**

Similarly, money as a resource (see Section 6.2.4) also affects CDM.

5.2   DESIGN

5.2.1   Appointments

At the start of design a client must appoint designers and a planning supervisor whom he is satisfied are competent and adequately resourced. Under some forms of contract, one or more contractors will be involved as designers (eg design-and-build, turnkey). This does not affect the requirements under CDM, which apply equally to these designers. The client, in appointing the design-and-build contractor, has to consider the competence and resources of the contractor to manage both design and construction duties (see Section 6.2).

5.2.2   Provision of information

Regulation 11 requires a client to make available information that he "has or could ascertain by making enquiries which is reasonable for a person in his position to make". The ACoP (paras 83–85) expands on this and leaves no room for doubt that clients are expected to be proactive in acquiring a whole range of information. It states that "clients must not leave it to contractors to discover hazards" and provides a list of the type of information expected. Where the existing health and safety file does not have the following, the client needs to collect the information on:

- characteristics of the locality that might affect construction
- hazardous materials, such as asbestos
- activities on or near the site
- requirements related to health and safety of the clients' employees
- access and space problems
- means of access to parts of the structure
- site services and their location
- ground conditions and underground structures etc
- known risks of instability or collapse
- previous structural modifications
- fire damage, ground shrinkage etc
- areas of poor maintenance
- restrictions on moving/using plant and equipment
- existing health and safety information from earlier designs
- as-built information.

Where a client does not already have access to this information, he is clearly required to take reasonable steps to acquire it, including commissioning work by others. Where a health and safety file already exists, this will provide a good start and is the first piece of information that the client should pass to the planning supervisor. Hence, it is better to develop a good file for a structure, to avoid the need for so much work if there is further construction.

5.2.3 Scheme design

As schemes are developed, site information should become available and the health and safety hazards and risks avoided or reduced as decisions are made about the scheme to be carried forward into detailed design. Residual risks should be recognised and carried forward to detailed design as information for further design work.

5.2.4 Detailed design

CDM actions that have started or should have started during scheme design must continue throughout detailed design. This may be complete before construction starts but often continues for some time as contractors or other specialists make their design inputs. In some methods of procurement (eg "fast-track") little detailed design may be complete before construction starts.

5.2.5 Planning applications, building regulations etc

The submission of formal applications for planning approval is a normal early part of the design process. Planning conditions imposed by the approving authority that affect the design (and hence the construction hazards) have to be considered as design instructions by the planning supervisor and designers. In a similar manner, depending on the project, various regulatory authorities may intervene regarding building regulations, fire, pollution, petroleum, heritage etc. Designers may discuss health and safety risks with officials and a planning supervisor may advise an official that he is in effect a designer with duties under CDM, but the conditions imposed will have to be complied with, even in cases of disagreement.

5.2.6 Other health and safety legislation

Consideration of health and safety issues arising from other health and safety legislation is a normal part of design and construction and it links into the issues addressed by CDM.

5.2.7 Pre-tender health and safety plan

Information about a project and its design that poses unusual or significant risks in respect of health and safety and which competent tendering contractors need to know is assembled in the pre-tender health and safety plan. This is normally prepared by the planning supervisor, whose CDM duty is to ensure that this is done before arrangements are made for the construction work (see Chapter 7).

5.3 CONSTRUCTION

5.3.1 Selection of contractors

Evaluation of health and safety competence and resources must form part of the process used for selecting contractors (see Chapter 6).

5.3.2 Appointments

Before construction starts, a client must appoint a principal contractor, who will normally, but not necessarily, be the main contractor. Contractors may be appointed some time before construction starts to allow them to provide input to, among other things, the development of the health and safety plan (for example, design-and-build).

All the appointees must be competent and adequately resourced for their work to the satisfaction of the client (see Chapter 6).

5.3.3   Construction plan

A construction health and safety plan must be prepared by the principal contractor. The client (normally with advice from others) must be satisfied that it is adequate before work starts on site (see Chapter 7). The construction health and safety plan should normally evolve throughout the construction phase, as circumstances change and as other contractors and designers provide information.

5.3.4   Ongoing design

During the construction stage, the planning supervisor will be involved in the co-ordination of designers' CDM duties and will collect information from designers as input to the health and safety plan and file.

5.3.5   Construction

Throughout construction, the management and co-ordination of health and safety issues is the province of the principal contractor. He is given wide-ranging duties and powers, which, in the interest of all concerned, should be aligned with the contracts of all the contractors involved.

5.3.6   Commissioning

For the purposes of CDM, commissioning activities up to handover to the client are all considered part of construction. The principal contractor will usually remain in control of health and safety on the site until handover. When a client assumes responsibilities for commissioning, handover will occur earlier and the CDM implications of this should be carefully considered and agreed between the parties. In such a situation, responsibility for health and safety on the site (the principal contractor's duties) must be confirmed or, if not confirmed, a new appointment made.

5.3.7   Health and safety file

Throughout the construction phase, the planning supervisor will need to ensure that information is captured and collected for the health and safety file, which must be handed to the client at the end of the project. The co-operation of other parties (principal contractor, contractors, designers) will be necessary for this work (see Chapter 8).

5.3.8   End of the project

The project ends (for the purposes of CDM) when construction (including commissioning) is complete and the works and health and safety file are handed to the client. For practical reasons, handover may be phased and the principal contractor will need to address the hazards and risks arising from this situation, jointly with the client/operator. (This has implications for the handing over of the health and safety file; see Chapter 8.)

5.4 POST-CONSTRUCTION ACTIVITIES

5.4.1 Rectification of defects

Normally, rectification of defects consists of minor activities during the construction contract defects liability (or correction) period. If these activities come within the scope of CDM (see Chapter 2), they need to be treated as a new project for the purpose of the Regulations.

Alternatively, if it is clear that significant work will continue after handover it may be decided to develop the construction health and safety plan to cover the continuing work and to manage the health and safety issues arising from the interfaces between the use of the structure(s) and the ongoing construction work. (This also has implications for the handing over of the health and safety file – see Chapter 8.)

5.4.2 Post-construction works

Regulation 2(1)(a) lists the following construction works as being covered by CDM if they fall within its scope (see Glossary):

- alteration
- conversion
- fitting-out
- commissioning
- renovation
- repair
- upkeep

- redecoration
- maintenance
- special cleaning
- decommissioning
- demolition
- dismantling.

> Note that any post-construction work **including maintenance activity** may be within the scope of CDM.

5.4.3 Cleaning

Normal cleaning activities (including window cleaning) do not fall within the scope of CDM, although the health and safety file should consider particular risks associated with cleaning (see Section 2.1.6).

5.4.4 Health and safety file

The file will need to be kept up-to-date if it is to be of continuing assistance to the management of health and safety (see Chapter 8).

6 Making appointments and judging "competence and resources"

6.1 MAKING APPOINTMENTS

6.1.1 The Regulations

The Regulations require that clients make appointments only where they believe (after reasonable enquiries) that the appointees will have the competence and resources appropriate to the task.

The CDM appointments that a client (or his declared agent) must make are:

- planning supervisor
- principal contractor.

Other appointments that a client may need to make are:

- client's agent (where required and appropriate)
- designers (whenever design is done directly for the client)
- contractor (all construction work contracted directly to the client).

It is good practice for the appointments of planning supervisor and principal contractor to be kept under review by the client, for their appropriateness and adequate performance. The term "kept under review" does not mean actively monitored; it means that the appointments should be reviewed if the nature of the project changes significantly, if the contractors change, or if a client becomes aware of inadequate performance. (See also Section 6.1.4.)

Any party that is competent and adequately resourced may fulfil the function of planning supervisor, including a client, a design company, a contracting company or a specialist consultant.

Any party that is competent and adequately resourced and that is (ACoP para 80) an organisation or individual that actually undertakes, carries out or manages construction work may be the principal contractor. It will normally be the main or managing contractor, as this gives control over the site and the other contractors.

It is good practice to make all appointments clearly, in writing, either in a formal contract (this is best practice, particularly for larger works) or, as a minimum, in a letter.

> Further guidance on making appointments is given in the CIRIA publications SP113 *Planning to build?* (Potter, 1995) and SP117 *Value by competition* (Connaughton, 1994).

For much construction work, clients will be able to judge for themselves whether those they intend to appoint are competent and adequately resourced from a CDM standpoint. This will be based on previous experience and guidance from their professional advisers. In assessing designers and principal and other contractors, they can call upon their planning supervisor (once appointed) for advice. If a client is unsure about making appointments under CDM one solution would be to appoint an adviser who has a suitable track record in the construction industry to act as a declared client's agent. (See Chapters 1 and 3 for more details.)

6.1.2 Timing

The timing of appointments of designers and contractors will be dictated by the project programme. The timing of the specific CDM appointments should be "as soon as is reasonably practicable" and as follows.

Client's agent

As soon as a client is aware that he needs help, he can appoint a client's agent and ensure that the appointment is declared to the HSE (see Section 3.1).

Planning supervisor

The Regulations are clear that this appointment must be made as soon as is practicable after a client has sufficient information about the proposed works to enable him to judge a planning supervisor's competence and resources, ie when concept design is starting. See also Section 2.3.1.

Principal contractor

A principal contractor must be appointed in time to prepare a construction health and safety plan that will be adequate for a client to permit work to start on site. Construction contracts should not be placed without a principal contractor being appointed and without an adequate period in the programme for a construction health and safety plan to be prepared before work starts on site (see also Section 6.2.3).

There may be considerable advantage to appoint the contractor who will act as principal contractor before the construction contract is signed, so that work starts on the construction health and safety plan before a formal construction contract is signed. This ensures proper health and safety planning, reduces the risk of delay to the works and avoids any pressure to cut corners in applying CDM.

Many contractors will proceed on the basis of a letter of intent; these vary in detail and are a matter for negotiation.

6.1.3 Form of appointment

From a CDM standpoint, contracts of appointment should, as a minimum, ensure that the parties are required to meet their statutory obligations under the Regulations. There are other issues that should be addressed, however, especially on larger projects (see Chapter 9). If in doubt, professional advice should be sought.

6.1.4 Changing appointments

Changes in CDM appointments may need to be considered if:

- changes in the nature or scope of a project occur that significantly alter the type of work, the hazards or the levels of risk such that a party is no longer competent or adequately resourced
- an appointed party fails to discharge their CDM duties adequately or in due time.

Clients or others making appointments are, of course, free to change their appointments for other reasons. Where the original appointee was named on the original form of notification to the HSE, an amended notification should be made. There is no statutory obligation to disclose the reason for the change.

One common reason for making a change follows the appointment of a design-and-build contractor. Then it may be reasonable and efficient for the contractor to be made responsible for carrying out the planning supervisor function, which may have been carried out by, for example, the client's lead designer while the project's brief was being prepared.

6.1.5 Nomination

When clients nominate trade or package (sub) contractors they are not themselves making an appointment. It can nevertheless be argued that nomination is "arranging to have work carried out" and thereby attracts client liability under Regulation 8(3). This requires clients to be "reasonably satisfied" that the contractor has the necessary competence to carry out the work. If the work is in the contractor's normal line of work and he has a reputation for good performance, this would be reasonable grounds for the client to be satisfied.

If a contractor had concerns on these grounds, the contractual requirements would be no different from concerns on other grounds, such as financial stability. A client would be unwise to underwrite the health and safety performance of a nominated party, if requested by a contractor.

6.1.6 Subcontracts

Companies to be appointed may subcontract work. It is not the responsibility of a client to assess the competence of these subcontractors directly, although the competence of a company to assess and select subcontractors may be a criterion for appointment.

6.1.7 Overseas companies

When clients or others wish to appoint (as designers or contractors) overseas companies that are not fully represented or normally active in the UK, there may be difficulty in assessing the level of health and safety competence and resource that will be available to the project. Clients should establish at an early stage:

- that the company is made aware of the Regulations, the roles it will have to fulfil and its duties
- how the company would fulfil its CDM duties.

6.2 JUDGING COMPETENCE AND RESOURCES

6.2.1 Sources of information

A client (or his declared agent) must judge the health and safety competence and resources of those he appoints under CDM.

Advice on competence and resources is provided in the ACoP paras 191–200.

> Further discussion of competence and resources may be found in CIRIA publication C603 *CDM Regulations – practical guidance for planning supervisors*.
>
> Clients may call upon their planning supervisor for advice about assessing the competence and resources of designers and contractors.

6.2.2 How to judge

The options are:

- track record
- references
- questionnaires
- interviews
- submission of documentation relevant to the project (eg CVs, outline method statements, resource schedules)
- spot audits.

Enquiries should be:

- relevant and reasonable
- guided by common sense
- appropriate to the project and its risks (ie proportionate)
- documented.

Although injury and enforcement statistics may be of interest, comparison of performance by this means is unlikely to be reliable.

> Very long questionnaires, the replies to which cannot be analysed in any useful way, serve no purpose. Enquiries that can be usefully evaluated should be focused on what is relevant to the work in hand.

For reasons other than the CDM Regulations, clients will wish to make properly considered, managed and documented appointments, because these are vital to the success of any project. The Regulations that apply to only one aspect of project management should not be allowed to dominate selection and appointments. The clear intention is that appointment under CDM should be an integral part of the assessments for the project.

The stages to be followed (listed below) could be compressed if a continuous client has a policy of making appointments from a list of preferred consultants and contractors. They are:

- specify the required performance: scale, scope, complexity, liaison
- identify the characteristics that will be important to fulfilling the performance. If using companies that have performed well in the past, consider whether there is anything different about the construction work in hand
- taking account of other aspects of a client's practice for making appointments, assess how the required characteristics will be judged
- prepare questions – the minimum necessary – to discriminate between possible appointees
- on the basis of the above, make the selection after making the necessary enquiries.

The essential elements are that the appointment process should be thought through and managed.

If a client becomes aware that a duty-holder is not carrying out his CDM obligations in a proper manner, he should take the following steps:

- formally warn the duty-holder
- obtain his proposals for improvement
- where these proposals are acceptable, agree a time for achieving improvements and record this agreement formally
- monitor the situation
- if not satisfied, terminate the contract and make new appointments.

The benefits for the client in taking this structured approach are:

- demonstration that health and safety issues are taken seriously
- better control of contractual implications.

6.2.3 Time as a resource

When assessing the adequacy of resources, it is important to consider the implication of "time". Ability to carry out CDM duties in a proper manner will be affected by the programme. Time is needed both to plan and to execute the duties. If a project has a tight programme, the duty-holders will need to demonstrate that they are capable of responding.

Of particular note is the need for a principal contractor to have time to prepare the construction-stage health and safety plan before starting work on site (ACoP para 87 refers) and to mobilise, including the establishment of welfare arrangements. Clients must allow sufficient time for this work.

As the programme is the primary control over the availability of time, it may be necessary to respond to time pressures by, for example:

- starting particular activities very early
- adjusting roles, responsibilities and procurement decisions
- overlapping activities
- taking innovative measures
- allowing more time.

The ACoP (para 200) states:

It is better to have a realistic completion date than an unrealistic deadline.

6.2.4 Money as a resource

The ACoP (para 200) states: "Clearly, clients need to allocate sufficient funds to the overall project for it to be adequately resourced."

It is therefore particularly important in the early stages of a project that the budget contains contingency and is not fixed at an artificially low level that may pressure the team to cut corners in matters affecting health and safety.

6.3 EXAMPLES OF GOOD PRACTICE

6.3.1 Demolition

Scenario

A factory site manager intends to create a car park, entailing the demolition of a steel coal hopper and a railway track. He is experienced in letting construction contracts and controlling work on his site but has no experience of demolition.

One good practice solution

The site manager decides that his company will act as client, planning supervisor and principal contractor, making a brief file note as to why he judges it is competent and adequately resourced to take on these roles. The site manager takes on an assistant to assist him in his CDM duties. He also engages a consultant with experience of demolition to assist in pre-qualifying a demolition contractor and examining the preferred bidder's proposal. Before appointment, the contractor is interviewed to ensure he understands the site rules so that factory personnel will be safe. Notes of the interview are copied to those present and put on file.

The site manager's approach is to take a proactive role, but to seek help in judging competence when he is not expert. He was particularly careful to ensure that those he appointed would be able to deal with the demolition in a competent manner.

6.3.2   Shop fit-out

Scenario

A retail chain leases a new unit in a large out-of-town retail park and needs to fit it out.

One good practice solution

The head office project manager co-ordinates the client's duties. The retail park's term facilities management (FM) contractor is retained as planning supervisor and principal contractor. Three fit-out contractors active on the site tender for the work on a design-and-build basis, working to a concept design and pre-tender health and safety plan provided by the retail chain's architect. The project manager prepares a brief file note recording why he considered each appointee to be competent and adequately resourced.

The project manager talks to the retail park manager about the other parties and interviews the facilities management contractor's site manager and the preferred fit-out contractor's named project manager and site agent. Notes of the interview are copied to those present and put on file to confirm how their competences and resources were judged.

> The project manager is working with appointees who are familiar with the site, but he satisfied himself that they are competent. In particular, he sought to ensure that the resources allocated would be able to provide the necessary competence to his project.

6.3.3   New-build office

Scenario

An overseas client wishes to build a new office on a business park.

One good practice solution

The overseas manager responsible for the project interviews consultants and appoints a firm as declared client's agent to act on his behalf in the UK. The firm demonstrates to his satisfaction that it has experience as client's agent and is familiar with the UK's health and safety legislation.

A consultant is engaged as scheme designer and as planning supervisor. As the overseas client requires a design-and-build contract, the selection of three firms to make offers includes the brief that they are to take on the roles of planning supervisor and principal contractor during the construction period. In the evaluation of potential contractors the consultant includes consideration of the contractor's capabilities for these roles as well as their capability to act as lead designer for the detailed design. The preferred bidder is asked for more detail and interviewed before he is appointed. Notes of this process are copied to those present and put on file.

> The client's agent is appointed based on his previous experience and his knowledge. As part of his assessment of design-and-build contractors he considers their capabilities for the CDM roles they will fulfil, taking particular care that the parties understand, and will be competent in, how to carry out their duties under the design-and-build form of construction contract.

6.3.4 Refurbishment

Scenario

An office manager plans to strip out all fixtures and fittings on one floor of a multi-storey building, after which various other firms will install new wiring and new fixtures and fittings to his design to a tight programme. He has never handled this scale of work before – although he has a good working knowledge of health and safety and risk assessment.

One good practice solution

The manager decides to appoint a firm of consultants to support him. The company he approaches advises him of his duties, as client, under CDM. He attends a course on CDM, including the roles of client and planning supervisor, following which he undertakes each of these roles on his project, but still with the support of the consultant. He calls for references that will support claims that they are competent to fulfil their designers' duties under CDM.

The contractors are firms used previously and in whom he has confidence. Nevertheless, they are asked to provide formal details of how they will manage their staff on site and also for outline method statements. He develops the pre-tender health and safety plan before they tender and selections are made, so that the interfaces between the contractors and the rest of the operational building are clearly understood. He appoints as principal contractor one of the contractors who is used to managing other contractors and will be on site throughout the work.

> The office manager has a hands-on approach; he likes to use people he knows, but he asks for information about the project to check that they are performing. He is particularly careful to check that they are experienced in handling the health and safety issues that arise when work involves several companies working to a tight programme.

6.3.5 Emergency repairs

Scenario

A property manager is telephoned with the news that a lorry has crashed into the wall of a shop and that the local authority requires that it be shored immediately.

One good practice solution

The manager asks the local authority for details of major contractors that provide a fully supported standby service, capable of assessing and managing the risks on site. He appoints the company that the local authority's chief engineer recommends as contractor and principal contractor for the work. He attends meetings on site to liaise and agree the work to be done. He asks his structural engineering consultant (who designed the building) to attend and to start work on a remedial scheme and he appoints them as planning supervisor. The manager makes contemporaneous notes of these activities in his work diary.

> When there is emergency, fast decisions are needed; the property manager therefore relies upon previous experience of the companies used.

7   The health and safety plan

7.1   LIFE CYCLE OF THE HEALTH AND SAFETY PLAN

7.1.1   Introduction

A health and safety plan provides for aspects of managing health and safety throughout design and construction of a project, developing as a project unfolds.

7.1.2   The pre-tender health and safety plan

The Regulations require the planning supervisor to ensure that a pre-tender health and safety plan is prepared and provided before arrangements are made to carry out or manage construction work. Normally, the planning supervisor prepares the plan, but other parties may prepare it under his co-ordination. At this stage, a pre-tender health and safety plan will amount to a collection of useful information, including surveys, significant design descriptions (where these have a bearing on safe methods of work and when justified by the circumstances) and advice on precautions to be taken to control significant risks. It is referred to in the ACoP and elsewhere as the "pre-tender" plan, because in many situations it will be passed to contractors at tender, so that they can take it into account as they plan and price their work. However, the ACoP explains (paras 150, 229) that whereas it may *also* be referred to as the "pre-construction plan" *or* the "outline plan", it is *always* (paras 67, 234) required in order to provide health and safety information to the contractor.

7.1.3   The construction health and safety plan

Once the pre-tender health and safety plan is complete and has been issued to contractors, it needs to be developed further into a working document to manage health and safety on site throughout the construction phase. This is the responsibility of the principal contractor. This document is referred to in this guide as the "construction health and safety plan".

7.1.4   Acceptance for work to start on site

It is the client's strict responsibility to ensure (so far as is reasonably practicable) that the construction phase does not start until the construction health and safety plan is adequately developed. A client may ask his planning supervisor for assistance when deciding whether to accept the plan and allow contractors to begin construction activities. The HSE advises that setting up on site is itself part of the construction phase.

7.1.5   Completion

When construction is complete, the health and safety plan has played its role and it ceases to exist except as a record document. Some of the information may contribute to the creation of the health and safety file (see Chapter 8).

7.2 FEATURES OF THE HEALTH AND SAFETY PLAN

7.2.1 An appropriate health and safety plan

If it is to be a useful document, the health and safety plan must be concise, focused and appropriate to the scale, complexity and levels of risk relating to the project.

The ACoP states, in para 237:

> *The aim of the pre-tender plan is to identify and target the key project specific issues, while avoiding unnecessary bureaucracy. It does not need to cover hazards that should be apparent to the competent contractor.*

Except for complex large projects, a good practice plan should have a core of no more than a few pages, although there may be appendices of supporting information. Long, unfocused plans containing pages of text-book advice about how to construct safely will be of no assistance to competent contractors and may obscure significant health and safety issues. For smaller projects, a single sheet of key points may suffice as the core document.

7.2.2 Pre-tender health and safety plan

A pre-tender plan is designed to pass to contractors information that they cannot be expected to know. Details of how this is to be achieved are set out in the ACoP paras 233–239 and Appendix 3. In outline the plan may contain:

- nature of the project (brief details)

- information about the existing site and environment

- information about the design that is relevant to health and safety during construction and that is project-specific or may not be readily apparent to the contractors

- significant health hazards arising from specified construction materials, which need to be drawn to the contractor's attention

- issues arising from overlap with a client's undertaking

- site rules, ie rules needed to manage issues arising from a client's undertaking

- procedures for continuing liaison by the principal contractor with the client and the planning supervisor.

A client's input to these subjects will relate to:

- provision of information

- particular requirements relating to the site and to safeguarding concurrent activities, persons employed and visitors

- arrangements for management and liaison

- any client safety goals.

Note that (as discussed in Section 1.2.9) if a client has particular requirements that fall within the ACoP definition of "design", the client will need to discharge designers' CDM duties (see Section 4.4.1). It is good practice for a planning supervisor to explain this and to assist a client to understand how to fulfil his obligations as a designer.

7.2.3 Construction health and safety plan

The construction health and safety plan is developed by the principal contractor as a means for contractors to plan and manage health and safety during construction. Details of how this is to be achieved are set out in the ACoP paras 240–247 and Appendix 3. Essentially, the construction health and safety plan will contain information drawn from the pre-tender health and safety plan, plus in outline:

- the particular approach for managing health and safety on the project
- the principal contractor's procedures for fulfilling his role during construction (this includes a number of detailed aspects including informing, consulting with and training those working on site)
- steps to exclude unauthorised persons
- site rules
- safe working procedures (including risk assessments and/or method statements as appropriate) taking account of other health and safety legislation as well as information provided by designers
- procedures relating to ongoing design
- common arrangements, including welfare and emergency procedures
- procedures for monitoring compliance
- updating procedures.

The construction health and safety plan is not a fixed document; it evolves as the planning of construction proceeds. The only interventions clients will normally make are:

- acceptance that the construction health and safety plan has been sufficiently developed for contractors to start on site (see Section 4.2.4)
- continuing liaison if the works affect a client's undertaking (such as shared access, noise etc) and/or if the site rules affect the client, his employees and his visitors.

A client may make specific requirements contractually binding by stipulating them in contract documents (see pre-tender health and safety plan above), providing responsibility remains with the principal contractor.

Although planning supervisors will liaise with principal contractors on matters relating to design (ongoing design, changes to design and design changes to meet new circumstances), principal contractors are entirely responsible for managing health and safety on site. Of course, a planning supervisor has a duty of care to bring to the attention of those responsible any concerns he may have about health and safety issues. Also, it is good practice for the principal contractor to consult with the planning supervisor about aspects of an evolving construction health and safety plan that would override important principles embodied in the pre-tender health and safety plan.

7.2.4 Non-standard situations

The life cycle described above will fit many projects – but some will be different. For each such project, a strategy will be needed to ensure that each of the parties is able to make its input in a suitable manner. Examples are given below.

Phased projects (such as a demolition contract followed by a separate construction contract)

These may be handled by treating the work as two separate projects, normally with a common planning supervisor, but with two different principal contractors (and notification of each). Each project would have its own pre-tender and construction health and safety plan. The health and safety file should be an integrated document.

Design-and-build projects

A scheme design stage before a contractor is appointed, should lead to an outline pre-tender health and safety plan. As the design-and-build contractor develops the design, his design team can then develop the health and safety plan. At a suitable time, the site management team will become involved and develop it further, to put in place the construction health and safety plan, before work starts on site. Before a client permits the construction phase to begin, he should check that the construction health and safety plan has been sufficiently developed in order to fulfil his duty under the Regulations. Further information can then be fed to the construction team by the designers, as design development continues, to inform the evolving construction health and safety plan.

It is good practice for non-standard situations to be dealt with on their merits to meet the intent of the Regulations. These two approaches provide examples of the variety of situations that arise in practice. See also Section 9.3, where this is discussed in terms of different procurement routes.

8   The health and safety file

8.1   WHAT IS THE HEALTH AND SAFETY FILE?

8.1.1   Introduction

The health and safety file provides information that will be needed by anyone preparing for construction and cleaning work on an existing structure, including maintenance, repair, renovation, modification or (finally) demolition. It contains essential inputs for future health and safety plans. It is prepared during design and construction and handed to the client at completion. The client is then responsible for making it available to anyone planning and managing future construction work or cleaning work on the structure and for transferring it to lessees or future owners of a structure. It therefore needs to be accessible and kept up to date as further work is done (ACoP para 263).

The health and safety file should not be confused with the operations and maintenance (O&M) manual. Under CDM, there is a statutory duty to prepare a health and safety file to provide ready access to the necessary health and safety information. For some projects it may be satisfactory for the health and safety file to be little more than an index to the O&M manual together with the highlighting of specific hazards.

> The file exists for the client's benefit. It ensures that essential health and safety information needed for future construction work is available and presented in accessible form. It is a "living document" that needs to be updated as further work is done on the structure.

8.2   PREPARATION OF THE FILE

8.2.1   The client's role

*   Determining content and format
*   setting it up with planning supervisors/designers
*   providing support within contractual framework
*   enforcing discipline possibly through payment control
*   maintaining it
*   making it available for future work
*   checking that it is updated when future work is undertaken.

8.2.2   What does it contain?

A health and safety file contains information about a project that may assist the planning and execution of future construction work and cleaning work. It will form an important part of the information to be provided by a client to planning supervisors involved in future projects affecting a structure. It may point to relevant information, eg to schedules of as-built drawings or to significant information in maintenance and users' manuals, but there is no need for it to provide comprehensive details that any competent contractor would be expected to know. See also ACoP paras 254–258 and Appendix 4.

8.2.3   What format and medium should be adopted?

The ACoP states (para 258) that the file may be made in any manner that will enable it to meet the needs of future management of the structure. Basing the file on an electronic media will assist with:

- security of the information (through backup)
- provision of information to others without risk to the original information
- updating and maintenance of the file.

8.2.4   How is it organised?

It is good practice for clients to decide how to arrange their health and safety file, because a well-organised file should be an extremely useful document in the life of a structure. It is the client's prerogative to decide on the file's coverage and extent beyond the legal requirements of CDM. The ACoP (para 258) notes that a client should discuss their needs regarding scope, structure and medium at the start of the project.

The health and safety file should be concise and well organised, providing ready access to information that reasonably competent persons might need for planning or executing construction work or cleaning work. It may consist of either:

- a single volume (or file) of information, which contains all the necessary information, or
- several volumes, which together form the health and safety file, in which the first volume draws attention to particular health and safety matters and makes reference to the other volumes. The other (supporting) volumes may include as-built drawings, operation and maintenance manuals and other information. Although the first and supporting volumes may be held and made available in different ways, they must all be treated as "the health and safety file".

The Regulations require that a file is prepared for each structure, but it does not specify the exact format. If a file is prepared for a project containing a number of structures, it should be easy to abstract the information for any particular structure. The extent to which a project may be subdivided, and whether it is envisaged that parts of the project will be transferred to new ownership at a later date, will influence how a file is formatted. Often this will be difficult to decide when the pattern of future responsibilities for cleaning, maintenance, renovation are unknown.

Each of those with responsibility must have access to a health and safety file. This does not mean that each of the 100 tenants of a complex should hold a copy, rather that they should know where a copy is held. A similar situation arises for groups of structures that might be managed by independent agencies and whose boundaries might change. Each circumstance will have to be thought through to ensure that the necessary information is available at the point of use.

Para 267 of the ACoP suggests that where a development contains roads and sewers that are to be adopted, they should have separate files. This demonstrates the common-sense approach to be taken.

8.2.5 Who prepares it?

The planning supervisor has to ensure that the file is prepared and needs the client's support in obtaining the information. Other parties (designers, contractors) have to provide the information that is needed. Exactly who prepares the file is up to the client; it will normally be the planning supervisor, the principal contractor or the lead designer, but could equally be handled by a documentation specialist. Whoever is made responsible must be competent and resourced and the responsibility made plain in contracts, and a programme for providing information must be established.

8.2.6 How and when is it assembled?

Information for the file should be captured from the start of the project – some of the information in the pre-tender plan may be useful (for example, information about contaminated ground). As design is completed and information from contractors becomes progressively available, additional input for the file is assembled, remembering always that competent contractors do not need to be forewarned of hazards they could be expected to anticipate. On large projects it may be prudent to keep the health and safety file separate from the bulk of the maintenance and as-built information so that important health and safety information is not swamped.

The final assembly of the file will normally be undertaken as the project nears completion. The planning supervisor will review and modify the file ready for handover to the client. This may not always be practical at handover, especially when clients seek early occupation, but it should be done soon afterwards. The project must be managed with this as an objective.

Clients should be aware that completion of documentation has traditionally followed project completion (ie handover to the client). Phased handovers will further complicate the situation. The Regulations require that the file (or parts thereof) are passed to the client at handover. In the event that some information is late, it will be necessary for the planning supervisor to pass the client an incomplete file with specific arrangements for the file to be completed. This may require contractual devices to bridge the gap between practical completion and statutory CDM completion.

Contracts should provide the spur to ensure completion. Experience has shown that best practice is to start compiling the file during the design phase and then develop it throughout the construction phase. It is important that information is collected before contractors who possess vital information leave the site.

8.2.7 How is it made available?

It is the client's duty to make the file available. This will include making it available to:

- designers and contractors for new work, when it will be the first piece of information to be passed to the planning supervisor
- contractors for maintenance and cleaning work
- any future purchaser or leaseholder of the structure
- any occupier of part of the structure.

See also ACoP paras 263–266.

8.3 CLIENT'S REQUIREMENTS

8.3.1 Introduction

As it is the client who is paying for the health and safety file and then holding it, using it and making it available to others, it is sensible that the client should define and communicate his requirements to the other parties.

> Most clients will have received as-built drawings and building services operation and maintenance manuals in the past; the file should be seen as a logical extension of this service, not a separate exercise.

8.3.2 Holding the file and retrieving information

The Regulations do not prescribe how the health and safety file is to be held and accessed. However, if the health and safety file (or an appropriate part of it) is to be made available equally to (for example) the window cleaner, the electrical maintenance man and to a designer of an extension, it will need to be subdivided accordingly and held as part of an active management system at the particular structure and not located at head office. Best practice is to hold a master copy at head office. Exactly how this is organised and subsequently managed and kept up-to-date is an important point for clients to consider in discussion with planning supervisors. For some projects, especially major ones, electronic media may be the way to hold, amend and access the data.

All the material referred to in the health and safety file should be considered to be part of the file and must be held and used as such.

Particular care will be needed to avoid a situation where a copy of the health and safety file becomes out-of-date but is still available for reference.

8.3.3 Leaseholders

Particular arrangements (ACoP para 265) need to be made when a leaseholder is involved, in terms of either:

- transferring the health and safety file or relevant sections of it to the leaseholder during the lease period or

- making arrangements for it to be available.

Whatever is decided, clients will need to think clearly how the following points are to be dealt with:

- security of the health and safety file, which is an asset of the client; and the absence of which may affect the value of the structure

- updating of the health and safety file as further work is done.

8.3.4 Disposal of property

A client who disposes of his entire interest in the property of the structure will normally (Regulation 12) need to pass the health and safety file on to the new owner, but he has to ensure the new owner is aware of the nature and purpose of the health and safety file. This will best be achieved by sending a letter referring the new owner to the Regulations and ACoP.

8.3.5   Updating the file

The health and safety file for a structure may evolve under the control of planning supervisors on future construction projects affecting the structure. However, clients need to think very carefully about how to deal with smaller day-to-day changes that may affect future activities – particularly if the consequences are hidden and potentially serious. For example, extending a wall or a surfaced area may have few health and safety implications, but details of rewiring part of an electrical system or other building services have to be kept up to date.

It may be necessary to adjust the file content on the basis of feedback from construction, maintenance or cleaning activity or following developments in technology or changes in legislation.

An up-to-date health and safety file will reduce the need for those responsible for future work to labour to gather information from scattered sources.

> It is best practice to maintain and update the file fully in all respects as a management tool and investment in the future.

8.3.6   Further guidance

Further guidance on the health and safety file is provided in:

- ACoP paras 91–93, 248–267 and Appendix 4
- CIRIA publications C603 and C604 (see References)
- HSE Construction Information Sheet CIS44.

9 Legal and contractual issues

9.1 LEGAL AND CONTRACTUAL ISSUES

9.1.1 Client responsibilities

Under the CDM Regulations, clients have the duties described in Chapter 4 above. Note that these Regulations sit within an overall framework of health and safety regulations, including the Health and Safety at Work etc Act, 1974, and the Management of Health and Safety at Work Regulations, 1999 (see ACoP p 96 for fuller listing); these other regulations apply whether or not CDM applies.

9.1.2 Sanctions

Failure properly to discharge these duties or otherwise to comply with the Regulations may result in enforcement action. Improvement notices or prohibition notices may be issued. Criminal prosecution may be initiated against corporate bodies or individuals.

Civil actions may also be brought. The grounds for actions may include the Regulations as follows:

- if the client fails to comply with Regulation 10, by permitting the construction phase to start before the construction health and safety plan has been developed, this confers a direct right of action for breach of statutory duty

- if the principal contractor fails to comply with Regulation 16(1)(c), by failing to take reasonable steps to ensure that only authorised persons are allowed on to the site, this confers a direct right of action against the principal contractor for breach of statutory duty

- evidence of failure to comply with statutory duties imposed by the Regulations will doubtless be cited as evidence of a failure to provide the standard of care required by civil law.

9.1.3 What does the client have to do?

A client has to appoint a planning supervisor and a principal contractor. He may decide to appoint a declared client's agent. All the appointments made, including designers and contractors, will need to be assessed for competence and resources, although if there is a long-standing working relationship with an appointee this assessment will be simpler to achieve.

A client has to document his response to CDM; see Section 3.2.1.

Other client duties under CDM, as discussed in Chapter 4, will need to be resourced or passed to a client's agent or otherwise contracted out. In particular:

- decisions about the competence and resources of appointees may be made the responsibility of a declared client's agent and advice may be sought from the planning supervisor

- provision of information may be delegated. For example, the acquisition of soils information will normally be organised by the designers. This would have to be properly arranged and resourced if a client were to be seen to have discharged their duty

- decisions about the adequacy of the construction health and safety plan may be made the responsibility of a declared client's agent and advice may be sought from the planning supervisor
- the holding and making available of the health and safety file may be sublet to a declared client's agent for that purpose.

9.1.4 Resources

Although clients may rely upon others to discharge the above functions, delegation and resourcing must be properly done and recorded. They should remember that sections 36 and 37 of the Health and Safety at Work etc Act 1974 enable the HSE to "reach over" an apparent offender to bring proceedings against others who have, by their own act or default, caused the offence. Bringing undue commercial or time pressures to bear might fall within these sections.

9.1.5 Contracts

Dealing with CDM in contracts requires a careful consideration of the roles of the parties under the Regulations, their interactions and contractual interfaces. The issues arising will vary depending on the type of work, the contracts used, legal precedents and (most importantly) the parties and their prior and ongoing relationships.

All parties are bound to comply with statute; this is an invariable obligation. It may be prudent to strengthen this with a contractual obligation that can be enforced by the client.

The contractual status of the pre-tender health and safety plan will need to be decided. It will normally be a referenced document. In some situations a client may wish to make certain of the requirements contractually binding on the principal contractor. In any event, the preparation and subsequent development of the construction health and safety plan will remain the responsibility of the principal contractor.

9.1.6 Statutory contractual relationships

Statutory responsibilities are binding in law. They cannot be set aside by contract, but a requirement to meet them may be made a contractual requirement.

9.1.7 Client's "named person"

It is good practice for a client to provide a competent "named person" for contact throughout the execution of any project. Similarly, other parties should be required to nominate focal-point personnel for health and safety issues.

9.2 TERMS OF APPOINTMENT

9.2.1 General

All appointments must be prepared so as to allow the parties to carry out their duties under CDM. This must include the right of the client to terminate an appointment.

9.2.2 Commercial

The forms of contracts used and their treatment of issues related to health and safety will vary. Thought should be given to the following commercial issues:

* right of access and powers of intervention by planning supervisor
* dispute resolution – to deal with disagreements arising from parties meeting their statutory obligations
* financial controls – to authorise payment of costs arising from consideration of health and safety issues associated with changes.

9.2.3 Client's agent

The duties of any client's agent must be made plain, as should any powers to decide issues or to incur liability for payments or acceptance of claims. Specific terms will be needed to determine and perhaps limit an agent's powers to provide information, make appointments, agree pre-qualification criteria, allow contractors to start work on site and to receive and hold the health and safety file.

9.2.4 Designers

There is a statutory requirement for any designer to comply with CDM. However, it is good practice to explain how designers will relate to the planning supervisor. The Regulations do not deal with timing of compliance. The appointment should cover this, especially for the provision of information for the pre-tender health and safety plan and the health and safety file.

9.2.5 Planning supervisor

Because this is normally the only appointment that relates solely to CDM (although the planning supervisor may also be a declared client's agent, a designer or a contractor), the form of appointment will need to be focused on the role (see Section 4.4.2). Regardless of the form of contract or appointment used, key issues include:

* liaison with and reporting to the client's project manager or representative
* provision of information by the client
* requirements for the provision of advice on the competence and resources of designers and contractors
* ensuring that designers comply with Regulation 13(2)
* co-ordination of the work of designers, both pre-tender and during construction
* the preparation of the pre-tender health and safety plan
* the preparation of the health and safety file, including the role of designers and the role of the principal contractor in acquiring information from contractors
* liaison with the principal contractor during the construction phase
* client's agreement to enforce the obligation of contractors and designers to co-operate with the planning supervisor.

9.2.6 Principal contractor

This duty will normally be made part of the duties of the main or managing contractor, but the relationship with the planning supervisor will require particular attention – see above – and the relationship with contractors appointed directly by the client should also be considered.

9.2.7 Contractors

Contractors' appointments, other than the principal contractor appointment, will normally be as "main" contractor or as subcontractor to that "main" contractor (see Section 4.4.4). It is good practice to make clear responsibilities for:

- provision and timing of information for the health and safety file
- safeguarding the site and preventing unauthorised access
- welfare facilities
- induction and other training
- emergency services
- consultation with operatives
- liaison with the client.

The "main" contractor's (head) contract should require that all subcontractors' contracts are aligned with the head contract.

9.3 THE ACoP

9.3.1 Status

As outlined in "The ACoP" on p 4 of this guide, the ACoP has particular legal significance alongside the CDM Regulations themselves.

9.4 PROCUREMENT ROUTES

9.4.1 Traditional

Clients who are comfortable with the "traditional" procurement routes will tend to appoint a planning supervisor as part of their design team. As confidence grows, this will increasingly be likely to be assigned to an existing (suitably competent) member of the design team. The duty may be transferred to the principal contractor when construction starts, to reduce the risk of misunderstanding and conflict between the planning supervisor and the principal contractor – provided that the principal contractor is suitably competent and resourced to carry out the role.

The principal contractor role will normally be assigned to the main contractor. Some clients may wish to carry out the duties themselves or assign them to others, eg the organisation acting as resident engineer. This option will be acceptable only if the individuals involved are experienced in undertaking or managing construction work of the type involved on the project and are adequately resourced. The reason for such a strategy will vary. Examples may be where a client is undertaking a phased development to be carried out with successive shut-downs by different contractors and wishes to maintain a tight and direct control of their operations on site, or where the client has a particular expertise that is considered essential to the effective safe delivery of the project such as works within a complex industrial process plant.

9.4.2 Turnkey and design-and-build

In the early stages of such projects, before the lead contractor is appointed, clients will need to consider CDM roles (declared client's agent, designers and planning supervisor). They will normally appoint lead contractors who are competent to take on the roles of planning supervisor and principal contractor from the time of their appointment.

9.4.3 Construction management and management contracting

There are many types of such contracts in terms of cashflow, responsibility and risk allocation. Once a contractor becomes part of the client's team the considerations outlined above for turnkey and similar contracts will equally apply.

9.4.4 DBFO and PFI

Again there are many different contractual situations that may arise. One particular aspect which will need to be decided is exactly who the "client" is at every stage of the project, from inception through design and construction, commissioning and after handover. The ACoP (para 56) states that a PFI "project originator" is the client. This requires that the project originator is proactive in carrying out all the client duties, either directly or by appointment of others. For example, each potential service provider's special-purpose-vehicle (SPV) could be a client's agent for their design. The project originator also needs to ensure that all the necessary information (see Section 5.2.2) is provided to all the potential service providers. So, before setting up the SPV, there may in effect be a series of similar but independent projects under way, each with its own effective client's agent (potential or "shadow" SPVs). PFI is discussed in the ACoP, paras 68–72.

9.4.5 PPP

As each public-private partnership (PPP) arrangement is a one-off arrangement, it is not possible to discuss how CDM will be applied. However, it is vital that the CDM "client" is identified and effective during the bidding or negotiation process and that they then put in place the necessary CDM appointments and mechanisms. PPP is mentioned in the ACoP, paras 68–72.

9.4.6 Partnering, term and call-off

The ACoP (para 39) mentions term contracts and notes that although CDM does not necessarily apply, the application of CDM to "each block of work" needs to be considered.

Where a client has a long-term relationship with a contractor, the handling of CDM issues can be placed on a firm footing so that when work is needed it can rapidly be put in hand. This is relevant where emergency work is envisaged (eg public utility distribution networks).

Normally, the contractor will be appointed as principal contractor for work for which CDM applies and the safe working procedures that are developed will be applied to all the work undertaken.

For larger undertakings that call upon the services of a number of small companies to carry out their projects, the client's own staff may wish to retain control and undertake key roles such as planning supervisor and even principal contractor (but see comments in Section 9.4.1 above).

9.4.7	**Maintenance contracts**

Contracts for maintenance may be established through a variety of routes, the forms described in Section 9.4.6 above being most common and normally of the "term" or "call-off" varieties. Where clients use their own workforce to carry out maintenance work they must ensure that competency and resources are appropriate and that they comply with the requirements of the regulations appropriately.

9.4.8	**Small jobs**

Where jobs are small but within the scope of the Regulations, clients may rightly be concerned that costs may become disproportionate unless roles under the Regulations are undertaken by the project manager, a designer or a contractor – always assuming that they are competent and adequately resourced. Clients should seek designers and contractors who are competent to undertake CDM roles of declared client's agent (if required), planning supervisor and principal contractor.

Glossary

This section explains the common terms used in this guide. Where explanations have been extracted from existing documents this is noted.

Agent
A person whose trade, business or other undertaking (whether for profit or not) is to act as an agent for a client. Employees of the client who discharge functions on behalf of the client are not agents of the client for the purposes of this definition.

Approved code of practice (ACoP)
Health and safety codes of practice are approved by the Health and Safety Commission and have special legal status. The code associated with the CDM Regulations is contained within HSG224 *Managing health and safety in construction: Construction (Design and Management) Regulations 1994* (HSE, 2001, referred to as "the ACoP"). See also introductory text "The ACoP" on p 4 of this guide.

Cleaning work
"The cleaning of any window or any transparent or translucent wall, ceiling or roof in or on a structure, where such cleaning involves a risk of a person falling more than 2 metres."

[Reg 2(1)]

The health and safety implications of other types of cleaning work must also be considered.

Client
"Any person for whom a project is carried out, whether it is carried out by another person (a client's agent) or is carried out in-house."

[Reg 2(1)]

Client's agent
For the purposes of CDM, a "client's agent" is any agent or other client appointed to act as the only client. The appointment may be "declared" to the HSE, or not.

[Based on Reg 4]

Construction phase
"The period of time commencing when construction work in any project starts and ending when construction work in that project is completed."

[Reg 2(1)]

Construction risk assessment
The process of risk assessment (see **Risk assessment** below) applied by contractors to the construction process.

Construction work
"The carrying out of any building, civil engineering or engineering construction work and includes any of the following:

- the construction, alteration, conversion, fitting out, commissioning, renovation, repair, upkeep, redecoration or other maintenance (including cleaning which involves the use of water or an abrasive at high pressure or the use of substances classified as corrosive or toxic for the purposes of Regulation 7 of the Chemicals (Hazard Information and Packaging) Regulations 1993), decommissioning, demolition or dismantling of a structure

- the preparation for an intended structure, including site clearance, exploration, investigation (but not site survey) and excavation, and laying or installing the foundations of the structure

- the assembly of prefabricated elements to form a structure or the disassembly of prefabricated elements which, immediately before such disassembly, formed a structure

- the removal of a structure or part of a structure or of any product or waste resulting from demolition or dismantling of a structure or from disassembly or prefabricated elements which, immediately before such disassembly, formed a structure, and

- the installation, commissioning, maintenance, repair or removal of mechanical, electrical, gas, compressed air, hydraulic, telecommunications, computer or similar services which are normally fixed within or to a structure.

but does not include the exploration for or extraction of mineral resources or activities preparatory thereto carried out at a place where such exploration or extraction is carried out."

[Reg 2(1)]

Competence	Possessing, or having ready access to, the skills, knowledge, experience, systems and support necessary to carry out work relating to the construction work in hand, in a manner that takes due account of health and safety issues.
Contractor	"Any person who carries on a trade, business or other undertaking (whether for profit or not) in connection with which he:
	(a) undertakes to or does carry out or manage construction work
	(b) arranges for any person at work under his control (including, where he is an employer, any employee of his) to carry out or manage construction work." *[Reg 2(1)]*
	This includes subcontractors, main contractors, trade contractors, turnkey contractors, design-and-build contractors (etc). It may also be interpreted as including others who manage (but do not contract to carry out) construction work.
Control	Measure taken to reduce (or "mitigate") risk.
DBFO	Design, build, finance and operate; a form of procurement.
Declared client's agent	See **Client's agent**.
Demolition and dismantling	Defined in the ACoP (para 30) as including the deliberate pulling down, destruction or taking apart of a structure (and) dismantling for re-erection or reuse.
Design	"Design in relation to any structure, includes drawings, design details, specifications and bill of quantities (including specification of articles or substances) in relation to the structure." *[Reg 2(1)]*
Designer	"Any person who carries on a trade, business or other undertaking in connection with which he prepares a design relating to a structure or part of a structure." *[Reg 2(1)]*
	This includes not only design professionals but also others who make decisions about materials or how construction work will be done.
Design risk assessment	The process of risk assessment (see **Risk assessment** below) applied by designers to their design.
Developer	For the purposes of the CDM Regulations, "developer" has a special meaning (see Reg 5), "when commercial developers sell domestic premises before the project is complete and arrange for construction work to be carried out", whereby the Regulations apply as if the developer were client and the work is not treated as being for a domestic client. In other words, a commercial housing developer is the client for the housing development even though he may have sold some or all of the properties before completion of the works. See also ACoP paras 101, 102
Domestic client	"A client for whom a project is carried out not being a project carried out in connection with the carrying on by the client of a trade, business or other undertaking (whether for profit or not)." *[Reg 2(1)]* See also ACoP paras 94, 95
Fixed plant	For the purposes of CDM, "fixed plant" means plant and machinery that is used for a process; it is not part of the services associated with the structure or building services.
Hazard	Something with the potential to cause harm.
Health and safety file	A record of information for the client (and others who need to see it) that focuses on health and safety. It alerts those who are responsible for the structure and equipment in it of the significant health and safety risks that will need to be dealt with during subsequent use, construction, maintenance, repair and cleaning work.

Health and safety plan	A document that contains information to assist with the management of health and safety as the project proceeds. It has two main stages: pre-tender and construction. The pre-tender health and safety plan (normally prepared before the tendering process for the construction contract) brings together the health and safety information obtained from the client and designers. The construction health and safety plan details how the construction work will be managed on site to ensure health and safety.
HSC	Health and Safety Commission.
HSE	Health and Safety Executive.
Maintenance	Construction work done to keep a structure functioning. See also ACoP glossary
Method statement	A written document laying out work procedures and sequence of operation. It takes account of the risk assessment carried out for the task or operation and the control measures identified. The term "safety method statement" may be encountered, but it is not normally used in the construction industry. All method statements should take account of safety issues.
Notifiable	Construction work is notifiable to the HSE if CDM applies and if the construction phase (including commissioning) is expected to last more than 30 working days or will involve more than 500 person-days of work.
Person	An individual, a company or a corporate entity.
PFI	Private finance initiative – a form of public-sector procurement.
Planning supervisor	Defined in the Regulations as a person who carries out the function as defined. The planning supervisor is the person who co-ordinates and manages the health and safety aspects of design. The planning supervisor also has to ensure that the pre-tender stage of the health and safety plan and the health and safety file are prepared.
PPP	Public-private partnership – a form of public-sector procurement.
Principal contractor	A role prescribed by the Regulations. The principal contractor is a contractor who is appointed by the client. The principal contractor has the overall responsibility for the management and co-ordination of site operations with respect to health and safety.
Project	"A project that includes, or is intended to include, construction work." *[Reg 2(1)]*
Project manager	For the purpose of this guide, the project manager is the party responsible for the management of the project on behalf of the client. He may also be referred to by other terms such as "contract administrator" or "client's representative".
Risk	The likelihood that harm from a particular hazard will occur and the possible severity of the harm.
Risk assessment	The process of identifying hazards, assessing the degree of risk associated with them and identifying suitable control measures (see **Control** above).
Safety method statement	See **Method statement** above.
So far as reasonably practicable	To carry out a duty "so far as reasonably practicable" means that the degree of risk in a particular activity can be balanced against the time, trouble, cost and physical difficulty of taking measures to avoid the risk. If these are so disproportionate to the risk that it would be quite unreasonable for the people concerned to have to incur them to prevent it, they are not obliged to do so. The greater the risk, the more likely it is that it is reasonable to go to substantial expense and trouble to reduce it. If the consequences and the extent of a risk are small, insistence on great expense would not be considered reasonable.
SPV	Special purpose vehicle – a company set up to carry out a PFI project.

Structure

"• Any building, steel or reinforced concrete structure (not being a building), railway line or siding, tramway line, dock, harbour, inland navigation, tunnel, shaft, bridge, viaduct, waterworks, reservoir, pipe or pipe-line (whatever, in either case, it contains or is intended to contain), cable, aqueduct, sewer, sewage works, gasholder, road, airfield, sea defence works, river works, drainage works, earthworks, lagoon, dam, wall caisson, mast, tower, pylon, underground tank, earth retaining structure, or structure designed to preserve or alter any natural feature, and any other structure similar to the foregoing; or

• any formwork, falsework, scaffold or other structure designed or used to provide support or means of access during construction work; or

• any fixed plant in respect of work that is installation, commissioning, decommissioning or dismantling and where any such work involves a risk of a person falling more than 2 metres."

[Reg 2(1)]

References

Although the references given below were correct at the time of publication of this guide, note that such documents are liable to be updated, superseded or withdrawn. Readers are urged to check that they have obtained the most up-to-date references.

ASSOCIATION OF PLANNING SUPERVISORS (2002)
R/002, *Clients and the Construction (Design and Management) (CDM) Regulations – what you need to do*, 2nd edn
Association of Planning Supervisors, Edinburgh

ASSOCIATION OF PLANNING SUPERVISORS (2003)
R/001, *Basic guidance for clients on ensuring adequate resources*
Association of Planning Supervisors, Edinburgh

CONNAUGHTON, J N (1994)
SP117, *Value by competition. A guide to the competitive procurement of consultancy services for construction*
CIRIA, London

DAVIES, V J and TOMASIN, K (1996)
Construction safety handbook, 2nd edn
Thomas Telford, London

HEALTH AND SAFETY COMMISSION (1999)
MISC193, *Having construction work done? Duties of clients under the Construction (Design and Management) Regulations 1994*
HSE Books, Sudbury

HEALTH AND SAFETY COMMISSION (2000)
L21, *Management of health and safety at work. Management of Health and Safety at Work Regulations 1999. Approved code of practice and guidance*, 2nd edn
HSE Books, Sudbury

HEALTH AND SAFETY EXECUTIVE (1995, 2000)
Construction information sheets
CIS39, *The role of the client* (2000)
CIS40, *The role of the planning supervisor* (2000)
CIS41, *The role of the designer* (1995)
CIS42, *The pre-tender health and safety plan* (1995)
CIS43, *The health and safety plan during construction stage* (1995)
CIS44, *The health and safety file* (1995)
HSE Books, Sudbury

HEALTH AND SAFETY EXECUTIVE (1996)
HSG150, *Health and safety in construction*, 2nd edn
HSE Books, Sudbury

HEALTH AND SAFETY EXECUTIVE (1997)
HSG65, *Successful health and safety management*
HSE Books, Sudbury

HEALTH AND SAFETY EXECUTIVE (2001)
HSG224, *Managing health and safety in construction. Construction (Design and Management) Regulations 1994. Approved code of practice and guidance*
HSE Books, Sudbury

OVE ARUP & PARTNERS and GILBERTSON, A (rev) (2004)
C604, *CDM Regulations – work sector guidance for designers*
CIRIA, London

POTTER, M (1995)
SP113, *Planning to build? A practical introduction to the construction process*
CIRIA, London

ROYAL ACADEMY OF ENGINEERING (1998)
R5.10, *The long term costs of owning and using buildings*
Royal Academy of Engineering, London

WS ATKINS and GILBERTSON, A (rev) (2004)
C603, *CDM Regulations – practical guidance for planning supervisors*
CIRIA, London

Websites

<www.aps.org.uk>
Association of Planning Supervisors

<www.cbpp.org.uk>
Best practice site: search on health and safety

<www.design4health.com>
Interactive guidance toolkit for designers

<www.hsebooks.co.uk>
Search for HSE publications

<www.hse.gov.uk>
About the HSE

<www.hse.gov.uk/construction/designers>
HSE website devoted to construction designer issues

<www.hse.gov.uk/re*vital*ising/index.htm>
HSC initiative setting targets for reduction in work-related
deaths, ill-health and injury

<www.learning-hse.com>
HSE e-learning site; gives further links

<www.ogc.gov.uk/sdtoolkit/reference/achieving/ae_h&s.pdf>
Government guidance on the integration of health and safety into
the management of projects

<www.safetyindesign.org.uk>
Safety in Design (SiD) website; includes:

• CDM guidance for designers (by Construction Industry Council (CIC))

• Accreditation of health and safety training for designers

<wwt.uk.com>
Improved health and safety awareness campaign

Acknowledgements

First edition (R172, 1996–98)

Research contractor — The research work leading to this publication was carried out by **WS Atkins Consultants Ltd** under contract to CIRIA. The project manager was **Alan Gilbertson** assisted by **Tony Moore** and a number of other colleagues.

CIRIA manager — CIRIA's research manager for the project was **Dr Ghazwa M Alwani-Starr**.

Steering group — The research was guided by a steering group, established by CIRIA to advise on technical scope and presentation of content, and an expert panel.

Chairman

Mr C Heptinstall	Sir William Halcrow & Partners Ltd

Members

Professor D Bishop	Construction Industry Council
Mr L Carvalho	HBG Construction
Mr E Criswick	DETR Construction Directorate
Mr A Delves	Ove Arup & Partners
Mr B Donaldson	North of Scotland Water Authority
Mr P Francis	Highways Agency
Mr P Gotch	Babtie Group
Mr P Gray	Scott Wilson
Mr T Hetherington	Health & Safety Executive
Mr J McLernon	DoE (NI) Water Service
Mr A Murrell	Property Specialists
Mr R Oughton	FC Foreman & Partners
Dr L Smail	Bechtel Ltd, latterly Det Norske Veritas Ltd
Mr R Soloman	Wessex Water
Mr N Thorpe	Health & Safety Executive
Mr D Williams	Balfour Beatty/Senior Safety Advisers Group
Mr P Williams	Liverpool John Moores University
Mr H Hosker	Building Design Partnership
Mr I Neil	Hyder Consulting Ltd

Expert panel

Mr N Blanchard	Conrad Ritblat Building Consultancy
Mr A Clarke	JR Knowles
Mr B Donaldson	North of Scotland Water Authority
Mr P Francis	Highways Agency
Mr T Maxwell	Procord Facilities Management
Mr A Pollington	Construction Clients Forum
Dr L Smail	Bechtel
Mr R Soloman	Wessex Water
Mr N Thorpe	Health & Safety Executive

Senior Safety Advisers Group

The following member organisations of the Senior Safety Advisers Group gave access to their sites and staff:

AMEC plc, Balfour Beatty Limited, Bovis Construction Limited, Clugston Construction, Costain Building & Civil Engineering Limited, Fluor Daniel Limited, HG Gleeson Group plc, Health & Safety Executive, John Laing plc, YJ Lovell Group Services Limited, Kier Group, HBG Construction, Norwest Holst Group Limited, Robert McAlpine & Sons Limited, SGB Group, Tarmac Construction Limited, Taylor Woodrow Group plc, Tilbury Douglas plc, Kvaerner Construction, Wates Limited.

Funders

This research project was funded by DETR Construction Directorate, the Health and Safety Executive, SADWSS (Scottish Association of Directors of Water and Sewerage Services), Highways Agency, DoE (NI), CIRIA's Core Programme and from contributions-in-kind from the Senior Safety Advisers Group.

Contributors

Valuable assistance was also provided by a large number of people and organisations in the construction industry. Particular thanks are due to practitioners who agreed to be interviewed about their experiences with CDM and to members of the Senior Safety Advisers Group.

Second edition (C602, 2004)

Research contractor

The book was updated in 2003 to align with the amendments to the Regulations in 2000 and the revised ACoP published in 2001. The contractor for this work was **Alan Gilbertson** of **Gilbertson Consultants Limited**.

CIRIA manager

CIRIA's research manager was **David Storey**.

Steering group

The updating was guided by a steering group, established by CIRIA to advise on technical issues. CIRIA and Gilbertson Consultants Limited would like to express their thanks and appreciation to all members of the project steering group and their organisations. The steering group comprised the following members.

Chairman

Mr O Jenkins (chairman)	CIRIA

Members

Mrs E Bennett	Habilis Ltd
Mr G Briffa	HSM Ltd (for the Association of Planning Supervisors)
Mr P Craddock and team	Arup
Mr D Lambert	Kier Group plc
Mr T Lyons	Taylor Woodrow
Mr R Whiteley	WS Atkins
Mr S Wright	Health and Safety Executive